C L A N B O O K :
NOSFERATU

BY BRIAN CAMPBELL

CREDITS

Author: Brian Campbell
Developer: Robert Hatch
Editor: John Chambers
Art Direction: Richard Thomas
Artists: John Cobb, Guy Davis, Leif Jones, Christopher Shy, Drew Tucker
Cover Art: John Van Fleet
Cover Design: Aileen E. Miles
Layout, Typesetting and Interior Page Design: Aileen E. Miles

735 PARK NORTH BLVD.
SUITE 128
CLARKSTON, GA 30021
USA

CLANBOOK: NOSFERATU

CONTENTS

FOOD CHAIN	4
CHAPTER ONE: LEGENDS AND HISTORY	12
CHAPTER TWO: INSIDE CLAN NOSFERATU	40
CHAPTER THREE: NOSFERATU CHARACTERS	80

FOOD CHAIN

The music all sounds the same to me now. Sitting in the same crowded club on another pointless Saturday night, I no longer care whether it's Old Wave, New Wave, Goth, Industrial or some shitty techno dance mix — I can't even tell anymore. The same pounding rhythms shake the black frosted windows of the nightclub, the same taut young bodies writhe to the thunderous backbeat, and once again, I nurse my watery beer, regarding the sweaty mass of flesh before me as I have on too many previous nights to count.

Black's still in fashion — it always is — so I sit in the corner, a black leather miniskirt constricting uncomfortably around my thighs. When I was as young as the other women — girls — on the floor tonight, my legs were my biggest asset. Now I've just got a... well, you know. A big ass warming a barstool.

I rock my feet back and forth on a pair of "knock-me-down-and-fuck-me" heels, taking another sip of beer. When I was younger, nights like this used to seem adventurous. Now, of course, I'm pushing 30, the joke's gotten old, and so have I. My morning shift, processing checks at the bank on for-God's-sake-Sunday-motherfucking-morning, is just six hours away. I can feel a clock ticking away like a timebomb inside me. Time's running out, baby. Time's running out.

Smile as another guy goes past... hope he turns around and comes back... maybe hope he doesn't. Where did I go wrong? Don't get me wrong, finding company for a few hours isn't the problem. Once you lower your standards enough, anything's possible. But those thousands of Saturday nights I thought I had ahead of me when I was 19 have run out. No matter what the venue is for clubbing, I'm an outcast, by age and appearance — hunting for what I can get at the bottom of the pecking order, near the bottom of the food chain. I can't compete with the impossibly thin little Barbies all around me.

Barbie and her friends are wearing a lot of black tonight — sporting the archaic retro style I abandoned when I was 14. Maybe it's cool again now and I don't even know — Oh, God. Am I that old? Does it really show? Not behind the façade I wear. My makeup is immaculately done — a careful blend of pale white and Death's own black lipstick. My hair is teased just like a Goth queen the kids here tonight don't even remember. I've even got my lucky panties on, although their luck ran out a long, long time ago. Just as I start to sweat from the heat and desperate energy of the club, I realize that it's that time of the week where I go out on the floor and use the only marketable skill I've got left. I dance.

Once the motion starts, my doubts fade away. I don't care how pretentious it is to go through the same poses every week for the thousandth time in yet another dreary nightclub. I forget about the swirling clouds of collegiate angst that surround me. The music piercing my skull sounds faintly industrial, but I don't even stop to think what it is. I only hope that if someone's going to come and take me away from all this, he'd better damn well do it soon. If my dance doesn't work, I know how the evening will end: I'll stagger home to my housecats, read the spicy bits of another erotica novel and dream of killing myself. Someone please end this.

From the corner of my eye, I can see that my movements have actually summoned someone. Jet-black hair, black slacks, T-shirt from some band I can't quite make out and boots to die for. He's coming across the floor, right for me, flouncing around like he actually fits in, despite the tacky, tiny silver ankh he's got dangling around his neck. How long ago did that go out of style? And he's wearing sunglasses indoors — still. Loser.

Just like me.

He passes a scrawny little poseur kid, then suddenly turns his back to me to give the wannabe a shock. The kid jumps, dropping his drink as he scrambles for the door. Yeah, I know that move. He thinks he's Demon Lover, and I think he's playing the whole Goth thing up way too much. Like I should talk. But, loser or not, he is kind of cute....

A few other Barbies try to capture his attention, but he acts like he knows I'm watching him. *Going for the pity fuck?* I think. Stop that. He's coming this way. My dance of desperation continues, even though I don't know what song's playing, nor do I care. Oh. God, it must be retro night — they're playing "Tin Omen" again. He poses before me and sets out his opening line. I can't even hear it; I just laugh and keep dancing. He's cute enough to pass the time until I have to click-clack home. Which home? I don't care anymore because I'm intoxicated, both from the overpriced drinks and Demon Lover standing before me. Standing beside me. Holding me. I'm way too easy, and I don't care. *This is just wrong,* I think, and the whole time, I want it to happen.

A while later, we shuffle off the dance floor. Two drinks and a whirlwind of bad retro music later, he's taking me outside, and I'm playing along. Anything to get away from here. The passions I felt with such intensity 10 years ago start to resurface again, but they no longer surprise me. I've been through this dance enough times, going through the motions once again, that I'm willing to let him lead me back to his car. Ooh — a sports car. Color me surprised.

I trip and giggle with calculated timing as I lower myself into the bucket seats, wobbling on my heels. The seat belt clicks into place, and I adjust my black mini for maximum effect. He's sitting in the driver's seat in moments, and I'm letting everything happen way too fast. No need for a seatbelt... he's already got me strapped down and... a rush of adrenaline washes over me as he leans over to kiss my neck, pinning me down against the leather seats. Pinning me down *way* too hard.

It's a dream. Closely followed by a nightmare. I'm bleeding.

• • •

Honestly, I can't remember what happened next. I thought what I felt in the next few minutes would at least be erotic. Maybe there was supposed be intense fear, or a surrender to an overwhelming force, or at least pain. I just feel numb. It's just as well. I recall an awful lot of blood. Far too much blood, cascading over loverboy's face, his lips, my lips? I don't know. Something horrible happened, because I remember looking up at his face at one point, when he just wasn't so terribly handsome anymore.

Perhaps it's my mind that's reconstructed him as hideous. Once we were outside the club, his cologne probably smelled a lot worse than it normally was — I can't stand the stuff anyway. Once it started, Demon Lover was gone, leaving me with some Demon crouched over my unconscious body. My mind remembers it as something from one of those old silent movies. Gray skin, sharp teeth, long fingernails. And the smell. He smelled like a dead thing, so cold and shivering. Or was that me?

Or is that me now? My eyes are shut, and the concrete floor beneath me feels very hard. So cold. So very cold. My inside's feel like they're shriveled, my skin itches something horrible, and at the back of my throat, it's dry and... thirsty. Bright lights flash on around me. Then I make the worst mistake of my life, one even worse than getting into the passenger seat of that sports car. I open my eyes.

Y'know, when I was 14, I used to daydream about Lestat coming and taking me away from all this. You can tell from the way I was dressed last night that I had fantasized about vampires, and Demon Lover could probably tell. No wonder his act was so carefully rehearsed. I had never dreamt, though, that it would ever be like this.

Before me is a perfect mirror, 20 feet wide. My thick thighs are the least of my problems now. My raven-black hair that just wouldn't behave before is now a filthy, matted mess, falling out in clumps. My pearly teeth that I used to brush faithfully twice a day are decaying before my very eyes. Layers of skin are decaying, shriveling slowly into some kind of reptilian carapace. How many times had I looked over my face for the tiniest blemish or pimple? Rather a moot point now. The useless silk blouse I put on — how long ago? — now wrapped around a caved-in chest, my legs are withering within the leather miniskirt, my eyes are sinking into their sockets, and it's all too much for me to take in.

Then I realize I'm not breathing anymore.

The face I use to stare at every morning, noon and night, whose tiniest flaws were an integral part of my identity, is now gone. Whether my nose was a little too small or my lips were a little too thick and all the bullshit makeup tips I used to hoard throughout my teenage years are all irrelevant. I suddenly feel like a fool having wasted so much time on vanity, because no matter how bad I looked getting up in the morning, it was infinitely better than the caved-in, scaly, sunken-eyed, slack-jawed thing I now see in the mirror before me.

I am no longer me. I cannot be me any longer. I must become someone else. Because if I don't, I'm going to go absolutely stark raving insane.

The Demon I remember crouched over my body — it wasn't my imagination. It was real. And I can see in the mirror that he's walking up behind me, but I'm too weak to turn around. I want to hate, to spit in his face, to at least put up a fight, but then the first wave of pain washes over me, and the nightmare continues.

• • •

The last week is a blur of sense memories and brutal flashbacks. Waves of crippling pain, an intense recurrent hunger, and numb resignation to my body's metamorphosis. I would now give anything to turn 30. Instead, my body is trapped in this living death: My jagged nails will always be the exact same length, my matted rats' nest of hair will always be teased at the same pathetic angle, and my face will be smashed in the exact same way every morning. Forever.

After a week of twitching, crawling and lapping up blood from the floor, after an eternity of not being able to tear myself away from that horror in the mirror, I have finally woken up somewhere else: someplace underground, with running water and the distinct scent of moldering urine.

Trembling, I rise to my clubbed feet, balance on the now snapped and useless heels, and gather about me the woolen blanket my Demon has left for me. I'm actually grateful for the improvement. The silk blouse and lucky miniskirt are still with me, reminding me of who I used to be, but the plush flesh that once made me recognizable as "female" has largely withered away. I don't know what I am anymore. Once again, out of the corner of my vision, I can sense that Demon is watching me unseen. And it's so cold. So very cold.

A rat scurries away from me, oblivious to my presence, and for a moment, I can feel the life and energy pulsing within it. The nerves twitch, its blood pulses, and the Hunger wells up in me again. Not for flesh, or even blood, but for Life, so that I can keep animating the withered husk that is my body. Intuitively, my corpse crouches down as I unleash a wave of *mercy* and *pity* from the depths of my shriveled heart. The little beastie stops in its tracks, looks up at me and then scampers up onto my shoulder to twitch its scabrous, sore-covered fur at me.

My teeth are sharp and quick. Cold, sickening bile chokes in my throat, my jaw quivers, and I return what's left of the animal's carcass to the turbid, roiling river of shit that flows beside me. From the distance, I can feel my creator's approval. I've just passed my first test. *Life's a bitch*, I reflexively think, *but now I'm dead.*

• • •

Demon never shows himself to me. He just leads me on, like that first night in the club. I have no idea why — maybe he's got all of eternity before him and it amuses him. Maybe he has plans for me. Most of the time, it doesn't seem like he cares one way or the other whether I'll get killed or whether my shambling body will just stop moving entirely, but he watches me very carefully, like a cruel and demanding parent. Maybe I'm expendable in some plan of his, but it doesn't matter: Most of my attention is focused on learning my way around these tunnels below, hiding from the footsteps above ground and scheming up new ways to get blood. I know that if I fail, Demon will kill me; if not him, then any human being who saw me would want to slay me on sight.

Tonight, I'm back to the old hunting grounds again. No more rat blood for me; I've moved up the food chain. I've crouched in the shadows of an alleyway, noting how many steps it is to the grate behind me in case I need to flee. The shadows envelop me — with a thought, I can wrap their layers of darkness around me like the old woolen blanket I discarded a week ago. I crouch like an animal, like a beast, like the monster I am, and once again, from under layers and layers of pain, I open up my dark heart with feelings of *need* and *pity* and *mercy*. I appear to have a talent for it.

In a heartbeat (I presume, since I no longer have one), a ranting fool, a transient who's been wandering up and down the street 50 feet away asking for change, is peering down the alleyway. Minutes ago, he

was hurling bitter obscenities at the people who passed him by. The
living, happy breathing people walk briskly past him as though he's
invisible. Somehow, welling forth a wave of *sympathy* doesn't take much
effort. He staggers closer to where I'm hiding, probably wondering why
he thought that something useful might be here, completely abandoning
all reasonable instincts.

Darkness surrounds me, and my teeth are quick. I claw my way into his
throat, his chest, and scratch further up the food chain. I am cold, so
very cold, but as his blood and life trickles down my throat, I am suf-
fused with warmth, suckling at his throat until the smelly bag of his
flesh falls limp. An animal must kill to survive, and if there's one thing
I've learned from the last few weeks, it's this: I'm certainly not human
anymore. I am so much less and so much more.

• • •

Demon nods at me from the other side of the nightclub. No matter how
many times I come here, the music always sounds the same. Sitting in the
same crowded club on another pointless Saturday night, I no longer care
whether it's Old Wave, New Wave, Goth, Industrial or the usual shitty
techno mix — I can't even tell anymore. The same pounding rhythms shake
the black frosted windows of the nightclub, the same taut young bodies
writhe to the thunderous backbeat, and once again, I pretend to sip my
watery beer, regarding the sweaty mass of flesh before me with equal doses
of lust and pity.

Black's still in fashion — it always is — so I sit in the corner with a
black leather mini uncomfortably constricting around my withered thighs.
Of course, as I look at the mirror, I can see that it's no longer darkness
that wraps around me. It's a whole new look, not unlike the one that I
used to put on every night for a thousand nights during the inexorable
climb to the age of 30. But now I get to play Barbie, too. I've learned to
disguise myself as one of them. And I've even got my lucky panties on.

I don't understand the latest fashions, but with a thought, I can make
others think that I am the height of trendy. I've mastered the façades of
this pathetically simple pecking order. A cute, stupid college kid saun-
ters past me. I smile. I open up the instinctive *sympathy* that pulses in
my withered heart, and he stops walking past me. Like an animal, he is
drawn out of lust and desperation, liberally mixed with booze. I know
those feelings all too well and reflect them back at him.

Ken pulls up a chair and sits beside my Barbie-doll impersonation. He
doesn't care what thoughts are in my head, what feelings are in my heart
or even who I am. I can feel his Life pulsing through him. Some of his
blood is probably welling up inside his boxers right now. I throw out some
opening line, but the music is so loud that he doesn't hear, just faking a
laugh instead. I've sat, and I've watched, and I've learned this routine
over the course of many years. With a calculated stagger, I prop myself up
on my "knock-you-down-and-kill-you" boots and get ready to lead him into
the alleyway for a little bit of fun. My fun.

For all my suffering and misery and despair, I now know this place for what it truly is. There are a thousand clubs like this one. They're open every week, and I go through the same motions there from month to month. I passed 30 a long, long time ago and frankly don't give a shit. I finally know myself, what I truly am, and I've finally moved myself up to the top of the food chain.

CHAPTER ONE: LEGENDS AND HISTORY

*Beneath my feet then the earth must be tunnelled
enormously, and these tunnellings were the habitat of the
new race. The presence of ventilating-shafts and wells along
the hillslopes — everywhere, in fact, except along the river
valley — showed how universal were its ramifications.*
— H.G. Wells, *The Time Machine*

Sometimes, dead things won't stay buried. Dark secrets hidden from the curious have a way of resurfacing, like a dead body floating to the surface of a quagmire. Sometimes, corpses just won't stay dead, either — in defiance of the laws of man and God, they rise from the depths to walk the Earth. From the lowest levels of city sewers to the dark heart of the wilderness, these monsters creep from the shadows to prey upon the human race. Their appearance is shocking; their stench is atrocious; their behavior is unquestionably alien. They are the grotesque monsters known as the *Nosferatu*.

Like most Kindred, Nosferatu hunger for the blood of the living and fear the light of day. Unlike their fairer brethren, Nosferatu are doomed to hide themselves from the world of men. Restlessly and relentlessly, they stalk the Earth until the Final Nights, the End Times of Gehenna, when the Ancient who created their race will awaken from torpid slumber to destroy them all. Let others speak of the romantic world of vampires; for these creatures, vampirism is undeniably a curse, a dark fate condemning them to an eternity trapped within a hell of their own flesh.

The Nosferatu have their origins in legend: They are the inheritors of an original sin as old as history itself. Aeons ago, the first Nosferatu created a childe out of passion, an act he would regret for millennia. That same passion later compelled him to rebel against the fiend who had created him, an act for which he was cursed until the end of time. From that moment, Nosferatu and all his descendants degenerated into a race of hideous monsters, shockingly abominable beasts forced to hide from the world of humans to ensure their own survival. Overwhelmed by remorse, the Nosferatu Antediluvian sent his eldest childer to hunt down and destroy the clan he had spawned. Since that time, the minions of Clan Nosferatu have stalked unseen, knowing that someday their progenitor will atone for his sins by destroying and devouring the last of his monstrous offspring.

This legend echoes through the sewers of Camarilla cities. It is a tale still whispered by broods of Sabbat Creeps as they undergo the Vaulderie, sharing their communal chalices of blood. Yet there is far more to Clan Nosferatu than either Camarilla Kindred or Sabbat Cainites suspect.

On the surface, the Nosferatu seem like such simple creatures. They are all undeniably hideous, twisted into physical degeneracy from the first moment they become vampires. Most are skilled at supernatural Disciplines for remaining unseen; a few have an ability to commune with the most feral and savage creatures in existence; nearly all of them have a talent for uncovering dark secrets others would just as soon forget. Yet beneath their tortured flesh, they hold even darker secrets in the depths of their foul hearts.

To Camarilla and Sabbat neonates, Nosferatu are simply disgusting creatures that skulk in city sewers, hunt in city slums or lurk unseen wherever Kindred and Cainites gather. Unfortunately, both societies are only familiar with a very small portion of the world. They are familiar with the world above but know little of the Nosferatu's labyrinthine warrens below. Misdirected by the obfuscative powers of slumbering Ancients, the elders and neonates of this modern world are oblivious to the vast kingdoms of giants in the Earth.

Above ground, two vast societies of vampires contest for dominance; both are unsure how to regard these bestial creatures. The first sect, the Camarilla, has a vastly exaggerated sense of its own power. Its history is inexorably intertwined with Western civilization, but the farther one travels from Europe and North America — the Old World and the New World — the more its influence wanes. Camarilla visionaries first traveled in the wake of human explorers, but whenever Kindred reached the edges of their maps — where imaginative men wrote the words "Here There Be Monsters" — they unearthed forgotten colonies of Nosferatu's childer. No matter how far the Kindred ventured from the safe and structured domains of Camarilla society, they still found Nosferatu hiding there, waiting for them there and

obeying instinctual traditions far older than the cowardly ways of civilized vampires.

The second society, inhabited by the Cainites of the Sabbat, was originally created in rebellion against the Camarilla's philosophies. Soldiers of the Sword of Caine frequently enlist Nosferatu as their allies, but they are just beginning to realize there is more to these creatures than meets the eye. Nosferatu Creeps are an enigma hidden under layers of wrinkled and tortured flesh. Those accepted into the Sabbat swear loyalty to the Sword of Caine — muttering oaths upheld by bonds of blood and reverently performed rituals — yet Sabbat Nosferatu are secretive, skulking, curious creatures.

The Creeps have a fierce habit of skulking off to commune with their own kind whenever they can. Nosferatu who ally with Sabbat packs will fight to Final Death to defend their allies, but they still demand places where they can be alone, contemplating horrors that only other Nosferatu can understand. They are at once the most bestial and humane clan in the Sabbat — masters of misdirection, silent hunters, secretive wanderers and, to the last one, overtly and unquestionably abominable monsters.

Outside the realms of these two vampiric societies, other vampires gather, plotting vast conspiracies against the human race and their own kind. Some nightstalkers whisper that they are autarkis, rejecting the dictates of either sect. Lurking nearby, the emissaries of Clan Nosferatu silently and obediently listen to them. Some profess to be anarchs, scheming to overthrow the elders of both vampiric societies. As their packs and armies gather, Nosferatu silently follow the vanguard into battle. No matter where the Children of Caine muster their forces, the silent and unseen minions of Clan Nosferatu are already there, waiting for them.

Removed from all these societies, Clan Nosferatu furtively gathers its own kind. Broods of Sewer Rats, Creeps and other horrors gather in the deepest realms of city sewers, the furthest realms of the wilderness or any secluded haven where they may scheme unnoticed and undetected by other vampires. Beyond any other affiliation, they are all Nosferatu, sharing a common curse and common needs for survival. Their purpose, their culture and their exotic natures remain mysteries to those who roam the world above. Now, at last, foul effluvia and fouler revelations are starting to bubble up from their labyrinthine warrens beneath the earth. From the dregs of vampiric society, from the depths of the sewers, occulted beneath torpid rivers of urine and feces, the dead rise again, showing themselves in their true and terrible forms.

Since the time of Nosferatu's eternal curse, his childer have skulked to the hidden and forbidden places of the world, fleeing the vengeance of Nosferatu himself. For the sake of their own survival, they have formed curious societies that transcend any boundaries of vampiric sect or philosophical Path. Some of these shambling, hideous corpses choose to rise to the surface world, but many of them have remained hidden deep within the shadows of the world, waiting for the Final Nights. As Gehenna approaches and the End Times begin, there is no longer a need for such eternal patience. Forgotten broods of Nosferatu are emerging from the shadows to take their place in the struggles of the night. Buried deep beneath human civilization for millennia, the dead once again walk the earth.

A HOSTING OF HISTORIANS

WE ARE LEGEND. For time immemorial, our history has been passed down as stories and tales from one generation to the next. As we crouch in darkness, hiding from the world above, we pass gossip, trade secrets and, most importantly, tell stories to pass the long nights of immortality. Millennia before the kine of this Digital Age developed their short attention spans, distracted by sound bites, infomercials, 22-minute sitcoms and commercial jingles, our neonates learned to memorize the saga of our clan: the hidden history of the world. Just as we have hidden our disfigured faces from the human race for all time, so have we hidden our legends.

Despite our observance of this tradition, many of our stories remain untold. Neonates struggle but simply do not have the talent to memorize our sagas word for word, as our forebears did long ago. The art of storytelling is being lost, notwithstanding the best efforts of those who struggle to preserve it. As each story is passed down, it is also distorted, embellished or corrupted. And worst of all, too many childer consider the stories of their clan simply that: Just Stories.

As Gehenna approaches, more of our elders disappear, never to be seen again, taking their legacies with them. Thus, while I still have the chance, I have given you the chance to listen and learn. We have gathered together a tunnel full of Nosferatu, a Hosting of historians, to chronicle the history of our clan. Together, neonates, they will help you understand who you are, where you came from and why we are all trapped here tonight in this dismal chamber far beneath the earth.

The Earliest Nights

Tusk, The Talebearer of Clan Nosferatu, begins:

I'll begin with the oldest legend — you already know how it starts. First among the vampires was Caine, damned by God for slaying his only brother, Abel. As punishment, Caine was cursed with immortality to reflect upon his foul deed and cast out of Eden for all eternity. I am told that, in that moment, Caine either called out the name of God or a pledge to God's Adversary; either way, Caine gained the power of the Blood, supernatural abilities that are solely the province of the Damned.

Caine created three childer and dwelled with them in the First City, known to many now as Enoch. Some say Caine himself was responsible for this haven's creation. Caine's three eldest childer called more humans into Enoch, so that the vampires could harvest the humans' blood and be strengthened against the night. The youngest of these vampires was named Zillah — because she was the youngest, she was also the most distrustful of her sire. Her older brothers, Enosch and Irad, were content to stay within the walls of the First City, but Zillah was curious about the world outside it. While tribes of kine were drawn to it, others fled from Caine's creation. The earliest mortals spoke ill of the city — it was a place where sin was plentiful and the laws of God were often cast aside.

Our chapter of the legend begins with a man who also did not trust the ways of Enoch. We are told he was a great hunter, a primitive who possessed such prowess that he sought to hunt the most powerful creatures in the world. The monsters that stalk the night in these, the Final Nights, are but distant descendants of the beasts he fought. The world has forgotten their names and their ways. As this hunter sought out the worst of the monsters of the world, he eventually found Zillah, the youngest of Caine's three childer, who preyed upon the humans of the city of Enoch.

This man, whose true name has long since been lost to the past, lay in wait for Zillah for a hundred days and nights. He lured her into the wilderness, near the mouth of a deep cave. Although he could not see her, it is said that he noticed her footprints on the ground as she followed him. Once he had lured her far away from the First City, into the chaos of the wilderness, he drove a wooden spear deep into her heart. But Zillah was not so easily defeated. With the strength of the Blood, she broke his spear in two; with the power of the Blood, she slashed him across his face, marking him with a scar that would never heal; with the fury that burned in her Blood, she smashed him against the rocks of the cave

with one powerful blow. His body, mind and weapon were broken, and he was close to death.

Yet Zillah was so impressed by his bravery that she thought she would reward him with the power of the Blood and Embrace him. She had come to hate her older brothers, and she knew that if she was to become more powerful than they were, she would need brave childer to aid her. And as she listened to the whispering of the Beast within her, she believed more and more that what she did was right. She looked down upon her childe with pity, and she renamed him "Nosferatu."

THE DOWNWARD SPIRAL

This hunter, Nosferatu, had once been a pinnacle among men, a titan who had triumphed over the most horrible beasts of the earth. Once he received the power of the Blood, his strength grew even more. He became mighty through drinking the blood of his prey, but he also learned to fear the three dangers we fear to this night: fire, sunlight and the treachery of men. For all his strength, he could not forgive himself for failing to slay Zillah. The mark on his face served as a reminder of his failure. Just as Zillah learned to hate her two brothers, Nosferatu learned to hate his sire as well.

Once Nosferatu gained the power of the Blood, he became a greater hunter than ever. Zillah's two brothers taught their own childer how to use the strength of their vitae, but Nosferatu was like a beast abandoned in the wilderness. In denial of his own descent from grace, he developed a terrible hatred of monsters. Nosferatu denied that he had become a monster himself, and exacted his rage on the lesser creatures of the Earth. And because he so hated the flaw ripped across his face, he learned to hide it, and himself, from any who would look.

Nosferatu soon learned to create others in his image. He taught his first childer how to hunt and how to look without fear upon the other creatures that roamed the night. While Caine's eldest childer commanded the mortals of the First City, Nosferatu preyed upon those who wandered in the wilderness. Before his Embrace, Nosferatu had become strong by destroying the most powerful creatures he could find, but after Zillah had baptized him into darkness, Nosferatu learned to become a hunter of men.

BOUND IN BLOOD

Now, legend tells us that Caine wanted to maintain control over his eldest childer, so to keep them obedient, he learned of the blood bond, the surest way to enforce loyalty. By forcing them to drink his blood regularly, his eldest sons became loyal to him, but by then, Caine could not find all the childer they had

spawned. In the same way, Nosferatu learned to make his childer loyal to him; by forcing them into bonds of blood, he gained a clan of obedient followers. And as he nursed his hatred of his sire, Nosferatu spawned dozens of childer.

Just as he had patiently waited a hundred days and nights to lure Zillah and destroy her, he created a brood of childer who would help him rise up and devour the monsters who had doomed him for all eternity. Just as the power of the Blood made Nosferatu strong, his hatred and remorse made him weak. When he roamed the night to hunt, he learned to treasure solitude because it was the only thing in the world that silenced the whispering of the Beast within him.

One night, in a moment of passion, he saw a beautiful woman bathing beside a stream. Again, her name has been lost from all the old stories; she now has a thousand names. He ravished her and drained her of her blood and then, because passion seized him, let her feast upon his blood as well. Before he could kill her and before he could realize what he had done, she fled. Unlike Nosferatu's other childer, she was free because she was not bound by Nosferatu's blood. Nosferatu was so furious that he gathered all his childer to him. At first, he commanded them to hunt this woman down and destroy her, but each night that they did not find her, his anger grew.

When his hatred was so fierce that he could no longer stand it, he finally gathered them to assault the First City. His eldest childer, whom he called the Nictuku, rallied around him and, with the silence of the grave, stalked the streets until they found Zillah and attacked her. And there followed a terrible battle. At its end, by the mouth of the cave where Nosferatu was first Embraced, Zillah smote down Nosferatu, leaving him broken and bloodied once again. Nosferatu's childer fled, fearing the retribution that would follow.

THE CURSE

Then Caine came to see what had happened. While Nosferatu nursed his wounds, Caine looked down upon him with the fury of a god. God himself had cursed Caine for slaying his brother, and now, Caine stood before another of his relatives, a chide who had tried to kill his sire, his mother, Caine's own daughter. At the sight of this attempted parricide, Caine was consumed with a vast and furious anger. And at that moment, Caine's hatred gave him strength: He cursed Nosferatu and all his descendants. Nosferatu and Nosferatu's childer and their childer's childer all fell down accursed by the fury of Caine, bearing a curse far more hideous than the flaw upon Nosferatu's face. And even the lone woman who had escaped into the woods, she too fell down, and her flesh withered, and her face cracked, and her bones warped, and for all eternity, she was to pass on the curse that Caine had placed upon Nosferatu.

Caine banished Nosferatu from the First City forever. Nosferatu crept away to hide in the woods once again, to return to the cave where he had first died and to sleep until he could dream of a way to atone for his great crime. Many years passed, and the Nictuku waited faithfully, bound through blood to obey his desire. And the woman who had escaped, the Matriarch of our clan, went out into the world to create her own family and become the sire of us all.

Time rolled on, and Caine's eldest childer begat 12 other childer, but that does not concern my story. A great flood came and destroyed the First City, and the Antediluvians slept beneath the waves until it passed, but neither does that concern my story. This is the end of the story: Nosferatu dreamt of a way to atone for his sin. As he slept, he summoned the Nictuku to him and commanded them to seek out the woman who had fled from him. To atone for what he had done, he would offer her up to Caine. But by that time, she had Embraced a multitude of childer, so Nosferatu pledged to destroy them all and offer them up to Caine. Nosferatu sent the Nictuku to slay them, one by one, and bring their ashes back to him so that he could make an offering to Caine and thus show his contrition.

It is said that we hide in the night because we fear the world of men. It is said that we hide from the light because we are hideous and ashamed of our cursed appearance, but this is not true. We hide in the night because we know that Nosferatu has sent out his eldest childer, the Nictuku, to destroy us all and offer our souls up to Caine. Caine's other childer know that the time will come when the Antediluvians will all realize the horror of what they have done and rise up and destroy all their childer and offer their souls up to Caine, but for us, the killing has already begun.

And that is why we crouch in the night, telling our stories, waiting and listening for the Nictuku to destroy us all. That is the story of how our clan began, and when the last of us has been found and destroyed, that will be the story of how our clan ends.

THE SECOND STORY: A SCIENTIFIC HISTORY

An autarkis cynic pontificates:

I DON'T BELIEVE IN LEGENDS. They might sound attractive, and they might help pass the time, but I know them for what they are: lies. Legends are told to repeat the lies our society is based on, keeping the eldest

THE NICTUKU ENIGMA

According to the Loremasters of Clan Nosferatu, the Nictuku are not a bloodline — they are eldest childer of the Nosferatu Antediluvian himself. When legendary Nosferatu rose up against his sire and her relations, he did so with the aid of his own blood bound childer. Although blood bonds have been known to wear off over time, legend also has it that Nosferatu has repeatedly renewed these bonds of blood, summoning his eldest childer to his torpid body, where they may feed and renew their loyalty. This is not without its dangers, of course: If the Nictuku did not have such a command of the Obfuscate Discipline, another vampire could attempt to follow them to their master and diablerize this Ancient. Thankfully, the Nictuku are allegedly powerful enough to erase all traces of their presence... if they exist at all.

One further aspect of the legend of the fourth-generation Nictuku has resulted in a great deal of speculation within Nosferatu society. Some legends state that before Nosferatu's curse, he Embraced a beautiful woman out of sheer lust, one who is now the "Matriarch" for the rest of the clan. If this is true, this mysterious "Mother of All Nosferatu" has never revealed herself; furthermore, she is not known by any one definitive name — Matriarch is simply the most common one employed.

Other myths claim that *three* such Ancients escaped Nosferatu's blood bond. This theory has some evidence to support it, since the infamous (and now deceased) sorceress Baba Yaga of Russian legend has been reputed to be a childe of the Antediluvian. If the Matriarch and Baba Yaga were the first two childer, then who was the third? Lore concerning Nosferatu's supernatural abilities provides one possible explanation: The highest levels of the Obfuscate Discipline, it is well known, can obscure all traces of a Nosferatu so thoroughly that he or she may be effectively forgotten. While there may be hints of legends that this creature once existed, many efforts to find such a monster are often forgotten or abandoned. The Nictuku Enigma remains a tantalizing glimpse of the clan's illustrious past — one as cryptic as the existence of the Nictuku themselves.

in power and the weakest in fear. They reinforce the status quo. We Nosferatu don't survive because of our ability to tell stories, we survive because of our cynicism and mistrust. It is my duty as a Nosferatu to keep that spark of doubt alive, and fortunately, the story you've just heard is enough to fuel that spark into a raging bonfire. If there's a story to be told, it should begin like this: *In the beginning, there was a great lie, and for some reason, we all believed it.*

I'll start with Fact One: There is no proof that Caine ever existed. Does that shock you? I do not believe that God cursed Caine; in fact, since I don't believe in God, that shouldn't surprise you. I was never a religious man before my Embrace, yet my sire insisted that we are all hideous because we were all cursed by God and Caine for some mythical, mystical, biblical event. Maybe Caine works as a *metaphor* for the first vampire, but the legend of how vampires came to be just doesn't make sense.

Why would God curse Caine by making him immortal? Why would God re-create him as the most powerful creature on the planet? Does that seem like *punishment* to you? I've heard from a few demented fools actually claiming to *be* Caine, but they've all been revealed as frauds. So, here's the next part of my story: *Nosferatu should not fear Caine because Caine does not exist.*

I am a Nosferatu, and by that, I mean that I am a species of vampire evolved to live in subterranean domains — no more, no less. I may be hideous by human standards, but so are many of the other creatures that hide from man. There are other types of vampires in the world, but they are far more prone to accept the standards of mankind. The oldest ones have formed communities to promote their own survival: The two largest ones are the Sabbat and the Camarilla. Both societies have stories about us being cursed by God and Caine alike. Both insist that we all have to band together to protect ourselves from Caine's childer. There is a reason for this: Both societies would just as soon exploit us for the sake of their survival, and oddly enough, I cannot accept what either of them profess.

I do, however, believe in evolution (like most kine in this age), largely because it is a theory that can be supported with scientific facts. If there really was a creature like Caine, he no doubt stumbled out of a cave, not out of some mythical utopia called "Enoch." From there, evolution specialized us into 13 major species; the story of Caine creating the 13 Antediluvians is, again, a facile metaphor for this fact. The Nosferatu are merely the species of vampire that thrived best beneath the earth.

A ROMANTIC HISTORY
A Camarilla Cleopatra explains the story of Nosferatu and Arikel:

Every Nosferatu has a favorite story: I'd love to tell you mine. The Toreador have a rather fascinating tale about our kind, one that's supposed to explain why the two clans despise each other so much. It's said that before Nosferatu was cursed by Caine, he was beautiful; the Degenerates of Clan Toreador believe he even fell in love with an Antediluvian named Arikel. When he was made hideous, he was so ashamed that he could never show himself to his true love again.

Nosferatu, in his rage, hunted his own childer and forced them into hiding, but Arikel celebrated the Embrace of her childer and taught them to revere beauty. Nosferatu's lost love, Arikel, created the Toreador, and apparently, they've pitied us ever since. Isn't that beautiful? I heard this story from a rather handsome storyteller, and he still repeats the story faithfully to me each night. You see, I've nailed him to a cross in my haven and kept him fed with my vitae every night. He will love me forever, as Arikel and Nosferatu never did.

As a result, we know the underworld better than any other clan. Long before the first cities of man rose, we claimed caves as our territory. In vast chambers beneath the earth, we rested, rising by night to feed on the living. No doubt this was the genesis of man's primal fear of the night, of darkness, of the legendary "monsters sleeping beneath the earth." Yet despite this, the Camarilla has created a lovely myth to comfort its childer shivering in the sewers. Through these lies, they attempt to keep us down there. Do you think our clan should be content with such a small kingdom?

If you were to ask me where we all came from, I'll tell you: We are descendants of the first life in the oceans. In fact, many Nosferatu still hide themselves beneath the water. We don't need to breathe, being dead and all; if we did, we would have choked on rivers of sewage long ago. Storm tunnels, viaducts, irrigation canals — whether filled with sea water, urine or chemicals, we can submerge ourselves in just about anything and survive. We don't trudge along the ocean floor, of course, since the pressure eventually gets too great —*at least for the more recent generations* — but I know many of you here tonight are going to shamble off back underwater when we're done here.

Yet for some reason, we're supposed to all congregate in the city sewers, presumably because of all the kine nearby. That's why the Camarilla and the Sabbat have added the story of Enoch, the First City, to their legends. There is no proof for the existence of the First City, either; thus, I have no reason to suspect it was ever real. Kindred scholars and archaeologists have gone looking for it, but even Aristotle de Laurent himself has never found it. I prefer to consider it another myth, one used to describe the way the first vampires controlled human society.

And, of course, as you've just heard, Nosferatu's eldest childer, the Nictuku, are supposed to be silently preying on our brothers and sisters. We've been told over and over that they are as hideous as they are ancient. Isn't that great? There's someone that's actually uglier than we are! Supposedly, the Nictuku are so preternaturally stealthy that they have never been seen, even by the Nosferatu. Thus, we're supposed to believe they're real because *no one can actually prove they're there!* Brilliant, isn't it? If you want to know why we all cower beneath the cities of the world, it's because the story of the Nictuku has been told and revised and retold over and over again. "Trust us," the elders say, "or we won't be able to protect you from the imaginary Nictuku!"

There's a moral to my story. You can choose to prop up the Camarilla and the Sabbat, but the only real reason to do so is for the sake of a good fairy tale. There's no reason why we should limit ourselves to wading through rivers of shit. In fact, there are plenty of us who haven't, and I appear to be the only one brave enough to come to this Hosting and say it. I firmly believe that we are ready for the next stage in our evolution, and it starts with leaving Camarilla cities like the one we're in now behind.

The tales of the Great Flood that almost destroyed the Antediluvians is sheer fantasy, as ridiculous as the tales of Nosferatu's curse and the Nictuku, but there is a whole world out there removed from the treachery of other vampires. Some of the autarkis have already begun venturing further out to sea, rising only as necessary to feed. I invite you to join us. The Camarilla has created a false history for you, a false sense of shame for you and a convenient place for you beneath their city domains. I reject their society utterly. I am autarkis, and I travel where I please. Beneath the water, beneath the Earth, beneath the feet of my lessers, I am Nosferatu; the rest of you who stay behind are the ones who believe in lies.

THE THIRD TALE: A CONSPIRACY THEORY

A Nosferatu architect creates a biased history of human civilization:

YOU'LL THINK I'M CRAZY, BUT I DON'T CARE. You won't believe me, but I'll say it anyway: For as long as humans have built cities, we've rebuilt them to accommodate our kind. For every massive city above ground, there's an underworld below it that the mortals rarely see. How else do you think the Nosferatu have survived for so long? Why else would Caine have given us such potent strength, if not to help us to build? Given the power of the Blood, the occasional ghoul to act on our behalf above ground and all of eternity before us, we have been steadily building our underworld since the beginning of history itself.

I know because I have seen it. Beneath the pyramids of Egypt, there are chambers that can be entered only by mists or shades, where Ancients rest in torpor awaiting the end of time. Beneath Venice, they are flooded buildings that have not seen the light of day for centuries, where Methuselahs do not need to breathe or feed but only to sleep and dream. I have crawled through the catacombs of Paris and Rome, where the undead stalk among the bodies of the decayed and subterranean ghouls reverently obey their every whim. Our world is the unseen, and we have been building it for centuries.

THE TIGRIS, THE EUPHRATES AND THE NILE

Even the most naïve neonate should realize that we haven't always lived in the sewers. The history of the Nosferatu goes back much farther than the history of sewage systems. The earliest civilizations, like those of the Babylonians and the Egyptians, were far more concerned with irrigation than waste disposal. As our autarkis colleague is so quick to point out, vampires don't need to breathe, so irrigation canals and viaducts were essential for hiding in the midst of civilization.

If you crack open a history book, you'll find out that the Egyptians living along the Nile carefully watched how the river changed over time, since this was crucial to their science of agriculture. We had to as well, I am told, because we built one of our earliest civilizations under that river — not much of one, but enough to keep us under the silt and away from the crocodiles. From a series of broods under the Nile, we raided for blood up and down the river. I have heard stories of other vampiric civilizations that existed during that time, such as those of the warring childer of Set and Osiris. That had little to do with us, though; in the same way our broods stay removed from the deadliest Kindred games, the Nosferatu of

Ancient Egypt refused to take sides. I am certain, of course, that doesn't mean we didn't occasionally sell secrets about one group to the other....

THE ROMAN EMPIRE

Ancient Rome was much better suited for our kind, largely because it offered us more places to hide. The Romans developed some of the first really elaborate systems for managing waste water because of their fondness for public baths. The cultural practice of regular bathing created a flood of excess water, see, and the Romans had to find a way to drain it from the city daily. Of course, public baths were also very amusing places for Roman Nosferatu to feed. A lone, naked, defenseless kine swimming in tepid water is easy prey. A Roman senator with his ass hanging out? Even better.

Rome faced a problem that all the really big ancient, and later medieval, cities had: storm runoff. During a season of heavy rainfall, all the water falling from the sky has to go somewhere, preferably away from people's homes. For both of these reasons, Ancient Rome originally used a series of surface drains to carry waste water and storm runoff into the Tiber River. I've heard that in parts of Eastern Europe, there dwell certain vampires who are unable to cross running water. Not the Roman Nosferatu — they would have died out! For the Sewer Rats of Clan Nosferatu, all that flowing water provided them with a perfect opportunity for feeding off a huge herd of kine.

As the cliché goes, Rome wasn't built in a day; instead, it grew steadily larger and larger over the course of several centuries. Ventrue and Malkavian elders have already taken a great deal of credit for that, but I don't particularly give a damn. What's important is that elder Nosferatu used their influence — a senator here, a wealthy family there — to help decide how all that excess water was going to be diverted. With all the politics going on in Rome, we also wanted to bring more Nosferatu into the city without requiring them to continually bother with using the Obfuscate Discipline. The Ancients tend to see around such disguises, right?

During the city's latter nights, the Romans decided that, because their surface drains were so terribly flooded, they needed to enclose them. The result was a series of long vaulted tunnels — the Cloaca Maxima — running through the most populous areas of the city. Let the other clans babble on about world leaders and major battles. This was one of the most important events in the history of our clan. Within three centuries, the entire sewer was vaulted, giving Nosferatu broods in Rome a chance to meet regularly and undisturbed.

AN UNTIMELY INTERRUPTION
Alexander Ruxard, a Nosferatu academic, politely interrupts:

PARDON ME! If I might just interject for one moment. Yes, you haven't noticed me standing over here in the corner, but I thought, if I may... if I may be so bold, I might point out a sort of a *footnote*, if you will, to your historical remarks. You see, I've heard other scholars aver that a very few ancient Nosferatu refuse to accept the fall of the Roman Empire at all! Because there are sections of Rome that have remained essentially unchanged, they've haunted the same environs for century after century, skulking beneath the city, surrounded by the corpses of the men and women they once preyed on. Other vampires have tried to displace them from this underground kingdom, particularly Necromancers desirous of the knowledge they guard, but such creatures would dare not abandon the catacombs of Rome. Oh, do forgive me... pray, continue....

The start of the Dark Ages was a major blow to the clan, but by then, some of the Cainites who survived were eager to re-create versions of Rome's Cloaca Maxima in other cities. Wherever Cainites conspired to help a city grow, if only for the sake of building a large herd of kine, it is likely there was a Nosferatu there wanting to influence where the sewer lines were going to go.

THE EUROPEAN MIDDLE AGES

As I mentioned, the next centuries were difficult times for us Sewer Rats. However, when the other Kindred stopped listening to the local Nosferatu, we eventually figured out that this water-management system we developed wasn't just a nifty way to sneak around town. It was also a weapon.

Long before the kine figured out the importance of good sanitation... well... we were already steeped in the subject (if you'll pardon the expression). In certain cities, broods of Nosferatu made the connection between the importance of diverting waste and the outbreaks of disease where they fed. After all, many medieval Nosferatu were... well... "bottom feeders" in medieval cities, soaking up blood from the lowest social strata. The poor and starving were often the first to suffer epidemics, and we watched their society as thoroughly as we watched the waste water that flooded out of a city.

Throughout the Dark Ages, many of the largest cities depended on the old Roman systems of waste

water management. When these fell into disrepair, the drinking water would get mixed with the sewer water. This would result in outbreaks of infectious diseases like cholera and typhoid. Science and superstition be damned — when you skulk around in the stuff, you tend to notice things like that! Of course, princes who didn't pay attention to such things were just asking to get blackmailed. That's part of where we got our sinister reputation. A Nosferatu elder could easily threaten a prince, and if he didn't listen, his kine would suddenly and mysteriously start to get very, very sick. A vengeful Nosferatu who continued this process along could hold an entire medieval city hostage, if need be.

A few of the more ambitious Nosferatu crawled up from the muck of European cities to feed on the other layers of sediment composing medieval society. Many of the other clans were what you might call "picky eaters," and prejudice, especially anti-Semitism, was an integral part of both Cainite and kine society throughout the Middle Ages. I'll leave it to others to speak of the Nosferatu broods that fed off the Moors of Northern Africa or thriving Jewish communities — I'm more of a plumber than a theologian or ethnologist.

The Importance of Waste

I can, however, tell you plenty about sewage. Nosferatu don't just muck about with sewers because they need a place to hide. Sewers, viaducts, storm runoff and waste management are all essential to the health of a major city. Pragmatic Nosferatu watch over this aspect of city management very carefully because it is essential to building a healthy herd of human kine. The more the city prospers, the more vampires can live there. Once more vampires gather in a city, like the Roman Nosferatu in their sewer system, the result is a thriving vampiric culture. Vampires swarm around a secure feeding ground like flies on shit, and they aren't that much further up the food chain.

If it weren't for us, all the Elysium toadies would be back in the Dark Ages, feeding off wormy peasants. Sadly, most major cities in the Middle Ages were especially unenlightened in the field of waste management. In places where the Romans hadn't built sewer systems, the first innovative attempts at organized waste removal involved privy vaults, usually constructed to serve several families.

Wealthy families knew how inefficient privy vaults were and thus preferred to live adjacent to or over a waterway or river. In Britain, London Bridge was a choice piece of real estate for precisely this reason. Of course, once we Nosferatu were granted domains in such a city, it suited us just fine, giving us covert access to wealthy homes the Ventrue never had. Unfortunately, privy vaults were often drained into the wrong sewers, since most kine were unaware of one of the most important aspects of sewage management. Hold it right there... don't lose that look on your face, because I'm going to keep you in suspense....

STAGNATING IN THE RENAISSANCE

With the birth of the Camarilla in the 15th century, the concept of sewers, waterways and viaducts as territory became a crucial one. Since the 15th century, some have tried to generalize a particular difference between Camarilla Sewer Rats and Nosferatu Creeps. Allegedly, Camarilla Nosferatu favor living below ground, while shameless Sabbat Nosferatu prefer blighted areas above ground. Such Kindred theorize that the Camarilla Nosferatu's carefully maintain city sewers to help a city grow; in contrast, the Sabbat Nosferatu allegedly favor destroying urban areas above ground to help a city decay. At the risk of offending some of you, I can give plenty of contrary examples....

Alexander Ruxard interrupts:

Um... excuse me... pardon me.... But I think you've gotten quite a bit ahead of our other guests. Your story is certainly very... um... fascinating, but perhaps we should give one of the other Sewer Rats a chance? Oh, no, forgive *me*....

THE SIXTH TALE: THE RAVENOUS MANITOU

A Sabbat Bestial confesses:

ENOUGH OF THIS SHIT. IT'S MY TURN NOW. Don't ever forget: We were hunters before we were ever monsters. Nosferatu was Embraced because Nosferatu loved to kill. That has always been our strength: feeding off the masses of humanity, draining them of enough blood until the swelling of their cities subsides. The Camarilla's pawns have done this by leeching off them bit by bit, but I have no patience for such a tiresome existence. Others will tell you how wonderful the cities are, but they fill me with loathing.

Four hundred years ago, I was Embraced in such a place: a cesspool called Rouen. At the time, Europe reeked with bloated cesspools where millions of mortals stumbled around waiting for vampires to kill them one by one. When I left for the New World, I told myself I'd never go back to the Old Country again. The thought

of exploring an untouched continent appealed to me. I hadn't realized that what I'd find there would be worse.

Humans fled to the New World in droves, and there were vampires willing to risk travelling abroad as well. I knew a few packs of nomadic Sabbat vampires who risked the trip in pine boxes, and most of them never made it. The risk was great, but not long after the colonists landed in New England, the Sabbat was there, ready to feast on the weak. At the time, I relied on the aid of a brood of fellow Nosferatu; the thought of hiding in a coffin for a few months didn't concern me much, as long as I had others to protect me. That's what packs are for. Some of us made the voyage in torpor; the rest had the cunning to go above the decks and feed at night.

My first few years in the New World made for the greatest time of my existence. The humans were far removed from the rest of civilization, so far away that we had no need to pretend there was a Masquerade at all. In one glorious orgy of blood, my brood could tear apart an entire settlement, drag the survivors back to our caves, hang them from the walls and drain them of blood for nights. Then, once the provisions ran out, we'd head to the next town.

Our fortune was too good to last, though. We thought we had the continent all to ourselves, but we were fools. There were other things out there in the woods, far older things than we knew about. We'd catch a glimpse of them once in a while, hideous beasts that attacked at night, dragging off one or two humans who'd strayed too far. Of course, the colonists thought they were prepared, blamed the natives, loaded their muskets and prayed to their God for help. Unfortunately, their God did not seem to care.

The ductus of our pack seemed to think that hunting down one of these beasts would make for an excellent ritus, and for some reason, we agreed with her. Maybe our "cabin fever" was worse than I remember it. One night, we decided we'd go out into the woods and hunt the local monsters ourselves, just to teach them a lesson. What we learned was this: The monsters were a lot like us. From the brief glimpses we obtained, we realized that there were Nosferatu in the New World and had been for hundreds, possibly thousands, of years. We eventually proved this by capturing one and torturing it for information.

Apparently, the bestial Nosferatu vampires that had been living there never really got out of the "hunter" stage you hear about in the old myths. The one we tortured kept babbling in his savage tongue about how he was going to devour all our souls, eat up the souls of the humans, feed his hunger — he kept raving on and on. We didn't understand his language, but he did seem to have a fantastic command of Animalism, so we shared at least one feral language. Later we found out that the natives referred to him as a "manitou," a spirit creature that feasted on spiritual essence. His methods of feeding were even more efficient than ours: All the primitives knew there was a monster skulking out there, picking them off one by one, but they would still leave sacrifices for him once in a while, just to keep him from going crazy and killing them all.

The manitou had a host of strange delusions. One of them concerned his choosing an animal as his "totem" and eating the souls of its children to gain strength. He'd find his totem animal — in this case, a bear — take over its soul and use it to go out and kill. Then he'd send his spirit back to the cave and set out again to hunt the bear. Maybe he was deranged, but to our ductus, it sounded like fun. Soon, we all realized that if we could learn to do what he did, we'd never have to leave the damned caves. Our pack spoke gloriously of commanding all the wolves around the primitive encampment, seizing all their spirits and setting out for the West, killing as we went.

We wanted his power, so we took it. We all gathered around his body and showed him how we committed diablerie in the Old Country. Then we tracked down his cave and found his tribe and set to work hunting humans from one side of the continent to the other. As you have no doubt heard, many of the packs of the Sabbat have adapted the practices of Native Americans into their ritae. We were no different. My brood learned to hunt like the manitou, and we've been collecting souls that way ever since.

COLONIAL AMERICA

Alexander Ruxard, Nosferatu academician, intrudes once more:

HOW THRILLING! If you don't mind, I should take this opportunity to add a *codicil,* if you will... an *addendum* to that rather exciting tale. For I would not want us to neglect the story of the actual *cities* of the New World, yes? As the kine continued to colonize early America, you see, they developed a series of small towns and villages along the East Coast, particularly farther north, in New England and like places. While Camarilla history seems terribly focused on places like New York and Boston, the large cities managed by elders and those sorts, few of us remember to include the story of the smaller towns, because typically, they're really more of a *Nosferatu* sort of thing. The other clans seem to go in for all the prestigious people and places, but we've been content to live in the cracks. At least, I have... I wouldn't *dream* of speaking for the rest of you....

At any rate, the most prosperous cities drew plenty of ambitious neonates wanting to make a name for

themselves as princes and primogen (or, more commonly, cardinals and ducti). The smallest towns were deemed beneath their notice. Who cared whether a town or village with fewer than a hundred people lived or died? Such places were tightly knit and typically religious, making it nearly impossible for Kindred or Cainites to establish a domain... unless, of course, they were particularly good at hiding their activities from mortals.

Antisocial Nosferatu found these quaint little burgs to be especially well-suited to their temperament. Sewer Rats who had traveled across an ocean to escape the politics of the Old World weren't terribly eager to tolerate the burgeoning vampiric gentry of the New World. New England and the East Coast supported thousands of tiny villages where a solitary Nosferatu could lurk and feed undisturbed. When I hear mention of Nosferatu Solitaries — as many of you young neonates no doubt will! — I think of this historical example.

Unfortunately, as is so often the case, many of these solitary Nosferatu could not resist the temptation to meddle with the local kine, sometimes choosing the humans of a particularly influential family as their herds. Just as Ventrue put their indelible "stamp" upon the wealthiest families of the largest cities, Nosferatu Solitaries ghouled isolated humans in the smallest cities. Since a Nosferatu ghoul often becomes unattractive or even degenerate from prolonged exposure to his master's vitae, the most inhuman Nosferatu created rustic communities whose squalor and decay reflected their own tormented souls. Thus, the Nosferatu are part of a hidden history of America, of the towns that failed, where slatternly women bred squalling children, where outsiders shuddered at the mention of incestuous families who passed along the same horrific taint from one generation to the next.

The Origins of the Camarilla

A former Camarilla Primogen makes a brief point:

Yes, yes, this is very nice, us taking credit for much of the history of the world and everything, but I think you've all exaggerated things a bit. Hell, we haven't even played that big a role in the history of *vampires*, let alone the history of the world. In Kindred society, the Nosferatu only really play two roles: watching and bitching. Since we're so far outside of Camarilla society, it's been our legacy to criticize what the other clans do.

I'll give you an example: the climax of the Anarch Revolt. 1493, the Convention of Thorns, near Silchester, England — Nosferatu were *there*, but hardly played a pivotal part. Josef von Bauren represented Clan Nosferatu, but from what I've heard, he didn't do much more than listen to speeches and pose. You'd have thought he was a Toreador, for all the good he did!

On the other hand, his archon, Federico, did far more than von Bauren did, because the archon sat and watched what was going on very, very carefully. While his sire postured and preened, Federico didn't really trust any of it. That way, he was one of the first to notice that the anarchs weren't all that keen on the idea of this society the rest of them were forming. If it wasn't for Federico's skepticism about Camarilla society, the anarchs would have had the element of surprise in their attack. Because he watched and bitched about how badly the whole thing was going, the Founders actually survived the Convention of Thorns.

I'll keep this brief, since my colleagues have a habit of going on for a bit: From the moment the Camarilla began, it's been our role to stay cynical, skeptical and doubtful. Because we're farther outside vampiric society than any other clan — well, except the Gangrel, now, I guess — we have a far more objective view of what's going on... and going wrong. That's my function as a primogen: to speak up when no one else realizes how messed up things are.

Of course, I'm not so delusional as to think that there's no Caine, like that fellow who seems to have disappeared from the room, but.... Hey, did anyone notice where he went? A few of us who were here appear to be missing. I think I'm going to take a quick look outside in the sewer tunnel....

The Historian's Addendum

Behold the return of Alexander Ruxard, Nosferatu Academic:

GOOD HEAVENS! I do hope nothing's wrong. Have we gotten to the 18th century yet? I can't believe that you've neglected to mention one of the most fascinating... simply most *fascinating* aspects of our history. I refer to 1789, more specifically Paris. Now, mind you, I've heard rumors that the Nosferatu of Paris assumed a part in the French Revolution, fomenting dissent against the aristos and such.

Allegedly, there was a brood of Sewer Rats there who hated the Degenerate vampires of the Parisian Camarilla with such fervor that they developed an underground conspiracy. Since that time, in a typically Victor Hugo sort of fashion, many criminals fleeing from the gendarmes have found themselves aided by unseen benefactors in the sewers of Paris, sympathizers who leave behind trails to facilitate their escape, food and water or even weapons to lash out at the hated Parisian Toreador and Ventrue. Simply *fascinating*, don't you think! Oh... oh, my, you're all looking at me in that way again. Do forgive me for interrupting....

The Eighth Tale: Within The Thieves' Citadel

A Camarilla Fagin brags:

THERE IS ONE CONSTANT IN THE EVOLUTION OF OUR CLAN: As human society has become more complex, we have had to become more ingenious in our methods of subterfuge. Without our wit and instinct, the kine would have flushed us from their cities like the Sewer Rats we are a long time ago. Fortunately, I have never been one for inhabiting such an obvious place as the sewers. My eternal curse began in the city of London, circa 1898. The exact year escapes me because I never had the benefit of a calendar. For that matter, I never had the benefit of a gentleman's education, indoor plumbing or the name of my mortal father. You see, before I was properly schooled in the ways of the world and educated myself in its iniquities, I am afraid I belonged to the "lower classes," as they say. I survived by means of theft, as a garden-variety guttersnipe.

For all its accomplishments, Victorian London had quite a few neighborhoods where the masses of human beings crawled inexorably into the gutter. History books are filled with glorious praise for what the aristocracy achieved, but in the city I remember, crime bred freely. There were hidden domains where the guardians of law and order dared not tread. The newest buildings were very attractive, but they often surrounded abandoned buildings and condemned tenements, creating complex mazes in the more impoverished parts of town. The desperate and the destitute lived in the alleyways and tunnels in-between, labyrinths above ground perfectly suited to the local Nosferatu. In my youth, my merry band claimed such an abandoned building as our own and fortified it against the local constabulary.

Street people swarmed to these places, especially since they were so easy to defend against intruders. In my dreams, I can still see the paths I used to tread: roofing precariously stretched across neglected yards and gardens; rickety walkways connecting the upper stories of rotting buildings; cellars accessible only through neglected tunnels. Only the inhabitants who were intimately familiar with the dangers within — from collapsing doors and floors to insidious deadfalls — entered with impunity. Deep within these mazes, criminals planned robberies, fencers stored their goods, fugitives cowered and the destitute scrounged. This was the heyday of the "rookery," the robber's nest: the infamous Thieves' Citadel.

Nosferatu fed freely in such slums because their stalking grounds had been forsaken by all the other clans. The humans would usually swarm into a few communal areas — typically hidden kitchens — where they could warm themselves beside trash-can fires. Once they ventured from these secluded elysia, they were easy prey. The kine slept in large numbers, sometimes 10 or 15 to a room, because they knew what might happen if they were left alone. I can still see the ambience of my favorite haunts: greasy windows, moldering floorboards covered with straw, walls tinged with soot and an aroma only a few shades more tolerable than the sewers themselves.

While it was possible for most of us to stalk unseen, some preferred to recruit others to do their dirty work for them. Ghouls are ruthlessly efficient, especially when thoroughly addicted to our blood. Turning the denizens of a rookery into a blood cult is childe's play. Once you found one ghoul you could command, it was easy to have him recruit another... and another... until you'd built an entire cult of them ready to do your bidding. The most ingenious Nosferatu developed entire blood cults of criminals and used them to spread their influence throughout the city. Dickens, of course, wrote a rather astute parody of our kind. Ever afterward, we were proud to call ourselves "Fagins."

Of course, the luminaries of this era, such redoubtable figures as Mithras and Queen Anne, were at first horrified to hear of the crimes our dens of iniquity encouraged. They changed their opinion when we began to contribute to the cause of the Camarilla. The Nosferatu of Victorian London were a highly organized brood, and between us, we developed an underworld whose tentacles thoroughly infested the city. The real pulse of the city was in the streets, and we fed rapturously from its veins. Thus, we were the most informed about the "word on the street" and traded such wealth carefully. The idea of the Nosferatu mastermind, the Victorian Fagin, soon came into vogue on the Continent as well. Throughout the civilized world, concentrations of Nosferatu soon bred concentrated criminality.

Of course, the Fagins of today are creatures I no longer understand. Perhaps my memories of my neonate days are hopelessly romantic, but now I find myself surrounded by new waves of foreigners, cheaply available handguns and drugs far more addictive than anything in my day. Gone are the smoky opium dens where we could expect to feed on the occasional Chinaman, the factories from which I could lure fatigued children. I welcome Gehenna, for I tire of this new age. Instead, I must content myself with reverie, remembering the golden age of the Nosferatu and the glory of Victorian London.

MORE HISTORICAL SHIT

One of our previous storytellers, an architect and plumber, interrupts:

WAIT A MINUTE! You've talked about the 19th century without mentioning the most important human of all: Thomas Crapper. You heard me, the inventor of the flush toilet, the patron saint of Clan Nosferatu. No, really — do you think that we'd have these vast warrens to skulk around in if it wasn't for *plumbing*? If you like, I can even take this part of our history a bit further back. All this fancy plumbing over our heads, all these tunnels that you crawl through, they're far more elaborate than anything the Romans had. All that was because of another hero, a scientist named John Snow. Now, I know you'll be disappointed to hear he wasn't a vampire, but when you hear what he *did*, you'll realize how much of what we have here is because of the kine.

The 19th century was the time when humans started realizing what we already knew: If you didn't manage your sewer systems adequately, disease would spread. I've made that point, haven't I? The Industrial Revolution made that concept more important than ever before. The increased concentration of human population, combined with the vast flow of industrial waste from their massive new factories, vastly advanced the need for complex and effective sewage treatment and water management.

John Snow was an English physician who proved this need scientifically. For a start, he used historical records to show how an elaborate series of cholera outbreaks could be traced from India to France to England over the course of several *centuries*. By illustrating how much damage these epidemics wrought, he set up the scientific community for his next important point: the descendant of the same epidemic was present in London, right then and there. In 1854, he proved that one recurrent outbreak could be traced to a public well called the Broad Street Pump — a rather fashionable Nosferatu gathering place in its day — and the reason could be traced to nearby privy vaults — remember those? — that had contaminated the water supply.

Snow was very methodical about his reports, but the English government panicked. So did many of the governments on the Continent; in many cities, European kine were required by law to release their waste into the nearest drainage system. Unfortunately, most humans, like most neonate Nosferatu, don't know the difference between the sewer system and the drainage system used for storm run-off. Remember what I told you about the Romans keeping the Cloaca Maxima separate from the waterways they used for their bath water? Remember the outbreaks of disease that

happened when those tunnels broke down? History, as it so often does, repeated itself.

The results were disastrous. The Thames was already turning into one big churning toilet, but because London's sewers weren't up to snuff, a reek filled the streets. One summer, someone finally had to put soaking rags over the windows of Parliament to keep out the smell. Okay, so maybe some of us Nosferatu got into the act and flooded the city with stench as well. We wanted more sewers, after all! As a result, the citizens of London began excavating a vastly improved sewer system, and we... well... we moved in to make sure it got built correctly. All thanks to John Snow starting a public panic.

As a result, our labyrinths have grown more over the last century than they had in the two thousand years before Mr. Snow. Despite all the evolution going on above ground, indoor plumbing didn't change all that much between the Roman Empire and the 19th century. But once we started flooding the cities of kine with the aroma we know so well, even the Camarilla princes started to take us seriously.

MODERN SEWAGE

Now that I've gotten your attention, I can at last tell you more about my favorite topic. Don't worry, I'll keep it brief. Many vampires who have never been below ground, including some in our own clan (ahem!) mistakenly think that all sewers are solely constructed for the disposal of filth and feces and that all of them harbor the same horrific stench. However, sewers generally fall into two categories: domestic (or industrial) sewers and storm sewers. The first deals principally with waste; the second is important in diverting the flow of water.

Some cities choose to combine the two systems, which is certainly less expensive, but the largest cities must keep them separate to manage them effectively. It's possible to send all of these fluids through the local treatment plant, but many systems have enough difficulty trying to process sewage without having to work overtime every time the city is besieged by rain. Many cities ensure that their sewage water never mingles with the storm sewers used to drain the city streets during rainstorms and floods. This means that it's possible to travel beneath a city without perpetually being hip-deep in feces.

And, of course, the Nosferatu below ground do more than "supervise" subterranean construction. There's horticulture, too. If you manage to stick around this Hosting for an extra night or two, I'll invite you down to the local fungal chamber to see what the brood has been doing down there. Some of you have already heard stories about Nosferatu deep underground pursuing bizarre horticultural experiments, creating a wide array of fungi, spores, slimes and molds. While this is certainly entertaining, it's also quite practical. Microorganisms and bacterial slime are essential for treating and purifying water. That's the cutting edge of waste water management: choosing the right mix of organic chemicals to keep purifying the fluids we trudge through each day.

Of course, some of us who specialize in sewage management have been noticing that a lot of the water treatment has been screwed up. The level of toxicity in the sewers has been increasing; I overheard a Lupine talking about "worm-taint" in the sewers, and it's got me worried too. But I'm not an expert in such things....

THE MODERN NOSFERATU
Alexander Ruxard, our academic, intervenes:

WELL DONE! You've brought us up to the dawn of the modern age. Now, we've given quite enough time to this fellow and his talk of privy vaults and storm sewers, but we've neglected much of the actual *history* of this time. We've certainly maligned the mass media for killing off storytelling, yet I should also point out that it has actually served to promote our clan's image. Before we conclude our Hosting of historians, I'd like to comment upon a certain *cinematic* treatment that was important during this time. The one image for which the Nosferatu are best known — in the world of the kine — is of the actor Max Schreck in a 1921 silent film.

When Bram Stoker's *Dracula* was released in 1897, it romanticized the legend of the vampire throughout Europe and America. At first, many Kindred were horrified, certain that this novel would shatter the Masquerade, but over time, it did precisely the opposite, presenting a series of lies that would allow the Kindred to hide in plain sight. Once the initial scandal passed, various Camarilla clans become envious, even jealous, of the Tzimisce for being able to whitewash their history so swiftly. The result was a long serious of imitations, particularly after the invention of motion pictures.

In the early 1920s, the German director F.W. Murnau attempted to make the first film adaptation of Stoker's novel. The plot was only loosely based on the novel, but it was similar enough that Bram Stoker's estate was horrified. A lawsuit followed. By the time the film was released, the name had been changed. The original portrayal of Dracula was replaced with a vampire that looked singularly familiar to many Camarilla vampires. An actor named Max Schreck captured the essence of the most infamous of the seven clans, and by the time the legal dispute was settled, the film had a new name, one that would spread the name *Nosferatu* almost as far as that of Dracula himself.

A POORLY CHOSEN TALE
Alexander Ruxard continues:

Before we leave the 19th century entirely, though, there are a few more topics I much touch upon briefly. For instance, there is the American Civil War, or the "War Between the States," as some of my colleagues would characterize it. Oral traditions confirm the existence of several broods of Nosferatu in the South during the Civil War. Some of the most outspoken among the clan harbored a growing contempt toward slavery in human society. This included scorn for the very casual attitude many Southern Kindred had toward their ghouls, many of which were former slaves. These ghouls were treated only slightly better than animals, and many of the Kindred who yet valued their humanitas found such practices particularly galling.

These same vampires now take credit for the "underground" that helped liberate slaves throughout the South. Allegedly, several Rats worked together to smuggle cursed ghouls and human slaves out of the domains of degenerate Southern Cainites. Some of the humans they saved were ideal candidates for the Embrace. Thus, during this time, the number of Kindred taken from slave stock increased throughout the United States. Ghouls rewarded with the Embrace, escaped slaves and freed slaves introduced new cultures into our clan.

From the back of the room, a strange growling noise begins to echo through the chamber....

One of the largest broods moved not to the North, but to the swampland of Louisiana, creating a cult in the depths of the Mississippi Delta. I should refer briefly to one of the most notable of these Kindred, a Nosferatu Bestial known as "Alligator Man." You have heard of him, have you not? He has hidden in the bayou for centuries, surrounding himself with alligators of remarkable size and strength. Although some would dismiss him as legend, he sleeps beneath the turbid waters, employing his reptilian allies as his eyes and ears. Perhaps in this we may find some connection to our Sabbat colleague's tales of the "manitou"?

Ah! And if I am to speak of the 19th century, I have neglected to mention the continent of Africa at all! Return with me back to the Victorian age, when European explorers, scientists and ethnologists ravished the continent of Africa. Travelers returning from African expeditions relate tales of tribes who worshipped the Nosferatu, degenerate villagers who gladly offered up their blood in unspeakable rites to sate the appetites of such devils. I am told that they remained unseen, acting as gods for these primitives.

Of course, when European explorers began to tame the "dark continent," these monsters retreated further into the wilderness, taking their devout followers with them. Legend has it that the eldest of these creatures lived in a vast series of underground caverns, surrounded by the wealth he had gathered from his vampiric descendants.... This Methuselah hoarded his wealth like a veritable Solomon... leading to the legends of "King Solomon's Mines"....

An African Nosferatu fights off frenzy:

ENOUGH! I've heard you babbling about the history of "our kind," but your Hosting has neglected to mention about HALF OF THE PLANET! I've had enough shit for tonight — your hospitality in this cesspool is bad enough, but listening to this is more than I can stomach! Old World and New World? You know nothing of Africa. I will explain. Yes, that's right, now that you can see me, you can tell I'm not as pale as you. Congratulations, you've flushed out the colored Nosferatu at your little Hosting. The least you can do after being so rude is listen to me tell you the *real* history of the Nosferatu....

NOSFERATU KINGDOMS OF AFRICA

You've done an admirable job of rewriting history, but because most of you kowtow to the lords of the Camarilla, I don't think you can see much farther than Europe and North America. Ancient vampires didn't just feed off cities in those places; they sired childer all over the world. Maybe the other vampires felt safest in filth-dens like Rome, Greece and Carthage, but the Nosferatu who skulked around those empires deserved what they got — existing at the bottom of the food chain. Not all of us were content to cower in the Cloaca Maxima. In other parts of the world — realms the other societies of vampires rejected — we found a much better way of life. Nosferatu thrive in all the forgotten and abandoned places of the world. In Ancient Rome, you cowered in the sewers, but in Africa, we were once kings.

We were the *dyulamansa*, the Hidden Kings. We never deigned to rule the human race; we merely supported those who did. As long as empires prospered, as long as the trade routes carried slaves, salt, ivory and gold from tribe to tribe, our herds of kine were healthy. *Dyula*, vampires, roamed the wilderness of Africa protecting these caravans, trading stories and blood as we went. Gangrel wandered with us, as did other clans that have since passed from the world. Because few of your Kindred knew the secret ways and sacred paths that led across the vast Sahara, we had remained isolated from your Traditions, your precepts and your culture since the dawn of history. By the time your European explorers came into the heart of Africa, the *dyulamansa* had already been there for millennia, building a kingdom unto ourselves.

The Camarilla began in Europe, and in many ways, its always been a very Eurocentric society. Listen to the old histories of the Kindred, and you'll find that many of them are simply chronicling of events of the so-called "Old World" and "New World." The Kindred are only just starting to acknowledge — especially after their encounters with the Kuei-jin of the Far East — that vampires have existed throughout the world, not just in the cradle of what they deem "civilization."

History reflects the biases of those who compose it, and this is just as true for the Camarilla as any other society. In most of these sagas, "uncivilized" realms didn't really exist until European explorers added them to their maps. The Kindred and Cainites of Europe were often close behind, bringing their Traditions with them. Yet for them, the most amazing discovery was that wherever they thought they arrived first, *other vampires were already there*. Although the Camarilla is still loathe to admit it, paynim vampires were quite capable of developing their own civilizations without following the traditional methods of European Kindred.

Autarkis vampires were also common throughout these empires. European vampires who rejected the traditions of their elders had a strong motivation to leave the worlds they knew and explore the unknown. Nosferatu and Gangrel were often the most adventurous in this regard. While Gangrel are naturally prone to wander far from the safest domains of the Kindred, Nosferatu often fled to the "forgotten" corners of the world out of circumstance. The founder of the clan stalked the greatest monsters of the world, after all, and thus, his descendants understand the Disciplines of Animalism and Obfuscate well enough to explore where other Cainites fear to tread. Since Methuselahs were drawn to places like Rome, Greece and even Carthage, Nosferatu's descendants traveling far from "Western Civilization" was a simple survival instinct. The result was a series of colonies, broods and empires hiding around the world, including (as we'll soon unveil) the depths of the African continent.

The history of the Camarilla is the history of the West; it is not the history of my African ancestors. Far to the north, you hid in kingdoms carved beneath the ground, but our broods had no reason to hide. The Nosferatu walked among men, unchallenged by the arrogance of other clans. You have spoken of one African empire, in ancient Egypt, but most of you have never heard of the other kingdoms we guarded in the night. I shall speak of the generous empire of Ghana and the now-ruined acropolis of Mwanamutapa. Our empires had many names: Kanem-Bornu, Mali, Songhai of Gao, Mogadishu and Mombasa. Our populace included Nosferatu who had fled the world of European Cainites, outcasts who found exile in vast African kingdoms far from the madness of your princes, primogen, prisci and archbishops. *Dyulamansa* rulers were known by many titles in many empires — *kaya maghan, ghana, mais, chiroma, galadina* — by whatever title we assumed, we helped build the vast Nosferatu kingdoms of Africa.

EARLY CIVILIZATIONS

The beginning of my story would sound surprisingly familiar to your autarkis storyteller. It does not begin with Garden of Eden; it has no Adam and Eve, no Caine and Abel. The kine on which we feed today are the products of millions of years of evolution. If the current theories are right, the first human herds lived in Africa. Tell all the legends you want — in Southern Africa, there's evidence of *Australopithecus*, the oldest known hominid, living there over eight million years ago. The first *Homo sapiens* lived in Africa between 500 and 300 thousand years ago. Not long after that, there were several different African races living across the continent, herds of kine just waiting for someone to prey upon them. As they say in my brood, if there was a first vampire, Caine was probably black.

When the European kine wrote their history, they considered Africa chaotic and uncivilized, largely because they didn't understand its culture or history. At the end of the 19th century, for instance, European historians had a mania for ancient Egypt, but they wrote about it as though it wasn't a part of Africa at all!

Hardly surprising. Are you familiar with the "Hamitic Hypothesis?" In 1929, an American scholar claimed that any advance in African civilization was clearly the result of intrusion from the North. According to this worthy, all of African history was one long period of savagery and chaos, interrupted only by the introduction of new ideas from an early European race called the Hamites. Of course, the idea has long since been rejected. Such prejudice against race and skin color seems even more absurd to me now, especially after my appearance has been ravaged by Nosferatu's curse. Yet doesn't it seem equally odd that so many Kindred claim that human civilization couldn't progress without their help, either?

RISING FROM THE NILE

At least you've attempted to mention the Egyptians. Prior to 10,000 years ago, the lands that would be Egypt were buried beneath the Nile, along with the series of marshes, swamps and lakes that surrounded it. It is rumored that one of the eldest Nosferatu Methuselahs hid his haven deep beneath these waters, surrounded by reverent and obedient reptilian ghouls. He believed himself safe from the depredations of Nictuku, until he noticed in his torpid state that the land was gradually rising from the water, *bringing his body closer to the rays of the sun!* This Ancient grew horrified to see his underwater kingdom shrink day by day, but as the human farmers learned to cultivate the lands around his river, he awoke from his slumber and spawned broods of Nosferatu to protect him. His childer fed off the blood of these farmers, just as they fed off the lands of his domain.

The history your storyteller has given is mostly correct — not a bad job for a glorified plumber! You already know the tale of the two bloodlines, one serving Set and the other serving Osiris, waging war though their human servants. A fine story, even if it isn't true. Yet there are also legends of Nosferatu in these pharaonic kingdoms, stalking unseen as they fed and returning to the waters of the Nile before the rising of the sun. The Egyptian Nosferatu betrayed secrets to both sides of the conflict between the Setites and Children of Osiris. They had to because their ancient progenitor longed to conquer both races and regain control of his domains.

Yet there was also civilization outside of Egypt. We were much stronger further south. In Darfur, Kush and the other lands of Abyssinia, we guarded and instructed the chieftains and elders of African tribes. You call our activities the work of "cults," but we saw our duties as sacred. Kept unseen by the powers of the Blood, we often played a role somewhere between that of an ancestor, an elder and a guardian spirit. The "hidden kings" of these tribes saw that tradition was upheld and observed, and unseen, we made sure the storytellers who repeated the legends of our people remembered them exactly.

This is part of the origin of Nosferatu storytelling: We didn't start the practice to pass time in city sewers but, instead, to preserve the heritage of our herds. I know we are of the same Blood, for the Nosferatu of the Camarilla and Sabbat also know the importance of oral tradition. Loremasters would offer up tales before their

unseen ancestors, while further to the south, in the swamps and marshes of the Sudd-land, emissaries of our broods would gather before *our* elders, trading blood and stories as we would for generations to come.

UNIFICATION AND DOWNFALL

The mortal history is well known: The Egyptian Empire originally consisted of two states, one along the Nile and the other within the Delta. Then, in 3200 B.C., one king united both empires, assuming a double-crown that included the likenesses of the cobra of Lower Egypt and the vulture of Upper Egypt. The legacy that followed endured for a thousand years — a rather stable foundation for the development of Nosferatu tradition. In the history of the unseen, our culture developed such traditions as respect for the wisdom of elders, the importance of working in broods and the practice of hosting emissaries from other broods.

As Egyptian traders began to carry goods further south, the Cainites of Africa learned to take advantage of their activities. Brother Gangrel first learned how to feed from humans traveling along trade routes, since he could sleep within the earth nearly anywhere during the day, no matter how long a caravan's journey was. Nosferatu had a harder time on such journeys, but as the hunters they were, they went into the night unafraid. You may notice that many regular trade routes take advantage of rivers and other bodies of water — a rather convenient practice arising from our necessity for hiding places along such routes. In more remote regions, ghouled porters, askaris or animals would carry our slumbering bodies by day, and we would feed from them at night. In this way, we visited Nosferatu living even further from Egypt, solitary monsters who preferred to remain far from the cities of men, but still hungered for stories and news of other broods.

As these broods migrated, they hunted from subterranean caverns where they could gather and stalk in their true forms. Legends tell us that the Ancients of our clan commanded the very shape and substance of the earth, collapsing vast caves and caverns for the benefit of our descendants. Who are we to disagree if we do not know what the land looked like before these upheavals? A few unusual legends tell of the Song in the Dark, a psychic ability used to command vast subterranean creatures far older than our own kind to create for us vast havens beneath the earth.

Unfortunately, even if we possessed such occult powers, we could not roam as freely as the Gangrel, and over time, this limited our willingness to venture beyond our kingdoms. As time passed, one barrier deterred us from traveling to the north of Africa more than any other: the vast Sahara. Covering one-fifth of the continent, it kept our kingdoms isolated from the European societies of vampires, as much to our advantage as to our detriment.

The Ventrue may yearn for the glories of Rome, and Brujah still mourn the conquest of Carthage, but the eldest Nosferatu of Africa repeat legends of ancient Egypt. As hidden kings, we supported the reign of the pharaohs. Some elders claim we even helped supervise the construction of monuments to them. I find this somewhat incredible, but Nosferatu did grant us the strength of our Blood so that we could help build. I am told that in the seventh century B.C., when the Pharaoh Cheops ordered the construction of his Great Pyramid, Nosferatu ghouls were ready to lend their aid. Again, I personally find these tales far-fetched, but they do serve as inspiration for our childer to learn the arts of subterranean construction and the Discipline of Potence. If the Ancients assisted with one of the greatest wonders of the Western World, why should we not follow their example? We had no princes or harpies to teach us shame. We were hideous, but with our curse came that hideous strength that lies within our Blood.

The empire's downfall came from the Assyrians to the east and the Kushites to the south. I would like to say that the Methuselahs who slept beneath the turgid swamps of the Sudd-land commanded this, yet it is not our way to take credit for what the kine have done. Egyptian soldiers lost battles because Assyrian iron had a distinct advantage over Egyptian bronze; the legendary "four shadowy kings of Tanis" our Loremasters extol tore apart the secret societies of the pharaonic dynasty; the Kushites we watched over unseen exploited both of these trends. For two centuries, Kushite and Egyptian culture intermixed, and the age of the pharaohs came to an end. Of course, the influence of the Nosferatu kingdoms of Africa did not.

CARTHAGE

North of the Sudan, beyond the Sahara, the kine of Northern Africa had their own epic accomplishments. Camarilla and Sabbat history both speak of Carthage, but only as a conquered kingdom. Above ground, the Ventrue have spoken in their sagas over and over of how Rome defeated this vast empire in the Punic Wars. I surmise that it was not the collapse of Carthage itself that infuriates the Brujah elders — why would a neonate care what happened in the middle of the second century A.D.? — it is the incessant gloating about this event millennia after it took place.

The Phoenicians of Tyre founded Carthage in 814 B.C. on the northern shore of Africa. Nestled in the center of the Gulf of Tunis on a triangular peninsula, it

was ideally situated for maritime commerce. Well protected and easily defensible, especially with the nearby citadel of Byrsa, it harbored the greatest fleets of the Western world. For Nosferatu, however, it was somewhat less than an ideal haven. Because there were few hiding places within the city, the broods had to make their home (once again) in the ocean surrounding Carthage, rising from the wine-dark sea at night to stalk the streets unseen.

The Ventrue take credit for the greatest merchant empires, but it is by no means the only clan that understands how to gather wealth. Carthaginian Brujah hid in an empire that dominated trade throughout the Mediterranean. Then in the middle of the third century B.C., Carthage began to contest with Rome for control of seafaring trade. The result was the Punic Wars, lasting from the middle of the third century B.C. to the end of the second. In 146 B.C. the city was finally plundered and burned to the ground. Afterward, the Roman Empire forbade human habitation there.

The Camarilla is quick to repeat what a tragedy this was for the Brujah of Northern Africa, but it wasn't much easier for the Nosferatu watchers in the waters. Fortunately, about 25 years later, the Roman Senate decided to construct a colony on the original site of Carthage. The Brujah fumed, but the Nosferatu of Northern Africa held little objection. Rising from the waters, they soon gained some of the benefits of Roman civilization your plumber has already mentioned: storm drains, public baths, even an aqueduct for clan Hostings. The original colony failed, but Julius Caesar later sent a group of landless citizens there in 29 B.C. By 26 B.C., the Emperor Augustus centered the administration that watched over the province of Africa in Carthage.

Roman Cainites soon found what cunning advisors the Nosferatu of Northern Africa could be in regards to expanding their empire. We wanted more trade to support our African kingdoms, and for the next seven centuries, we had it with the help of Roman Kindred. Of course, the city passed through several different rulers over this time — the Vandals, the Byzantines and eventually the Arabs — but the maxim we repeat today was just as true then: The princes above ground may change, but the rulers of the underworld always remain.

FREEDOM

The collapse of the Roman Empire was disastrous for the Cainites of Europe, but south of the Sahara, it had very little impact. Europe developed a feudal system of princes and domains to try to preserve civilization and withstand the Long Night, but throughout most of Africa, the idea just never caught on. The Brujah may

have held a grudge about Carthage, but then again, most of them were dumb enough to stay around Europe for centuries afterward.

Forgive me, but so were many of the early European Nosferatu. Like the mortals of medieval Europe, the Nosferatu clung to ideas left from the Roman Empire. Because their sires spoke so magnificently of the Cloaca Maxima of Rome, they believed that Nosferatu had to remain content with the hidden places of a city, feeding off the poor, the destitute and the starving. The Nosferatu of Africa never learned such shame. Instead of hiding from European Cainites, we developed Nosferatu kingdoms hidden from the Europeans entirely.

Many Nosferatu, Gangrel and other vampires who didn't want to contest for power with the European Methuselahs and their minions kept moving south, deeper into Africa. Whether this was through choice or design is uncertain. Some of us believe that Methuselahs of our two clans (or possibly one of the Antediluvians) summoned us there. Most of us didn't do this out of a rejection of European tradition. Our African traditions were merely different than the ones in Europe.

To this day, the culture of the Nosferatu remains different from the treachery of the other clans. Another Cainite culture spread across the land, one based on mutual respect for elders, the importance of passing down oral tradition and *ukwangela*, our version of hospitality and generosity. I see many of the same traits here at your Hosting tonight, but such displays are done furtively or secretly. We had no European Ventrue or Toreador to teach us to hide what we did. The African Nosferatu valued freedom, not only for themselves, but for the kine as well. As part of this, we never attempted to control human empires, merely encouraging them to grow so that we could feed well. Unlike much of the Camarilla over the past few centuries, we never laid claim to the history of mankind; we skulked in the shadows of mankind's history, supporting the rulers and merchant kings that allowed our herds of kine to prosper.

While Europe decayed, trade routes continued to spread across Africa, bringing fresh blood into the continent's dark heart. Muslim merchants sent their trading ships from settlements in India, Ceylon and Malaysia west along the eastern coast of Africa and east as far as China. Knowledge of the trade routes was essential for Nosferatu emissaries carrying news from brood to brood. By night, vampires stalked the trade ships unseen, and by day, they slept in the depths of the cargo holds. China remained a dangerous mystery to us, but wherever a solitary Nosferatu shunned the company of his own kind, there was a chance to spread our spawn further from the domains of the Europeans.

Berber traders also ventured across oceans of sand, bringing goods south across the Sahara and deep within the continent. While the Gangrel were far better suited to these caravans (which often traveled by night), we welcomed them into our broods' domains, eager for any stories they brought with them. Oases and wells became essential to these trade routes; in the deepest ones, immortals slept, rising to feed from passing merchants.

Of course, Nosferatu kings felt safest in the largest concentrations of kine, and Africa had many thriving kingdoms from which to feed. The greatest succeeded because of their merchant caravans; the name most often used for the Nosferatu kings of Africa, the *dyulamansa*, is a term used to describe Muslim traders. We traded in merchandise; you trade in information; in this regard, we are not so different. African Gangrel felt at home along the trade routes, but in the cities of Africa, we were the strongest of the clans.

While the European Nosferatu of the Middle Ages fed off the outcast and impoverished, the African Nosferatu stalked the streets of the greatest cities in the world. Tales abound of their wealth and grandeur. In East Africa, the Kingdom of Kilwa was described by Muslim scholars as one of the most beautiful and well-constructed in the world, exceeding even the glorious cities of India and China. Medieval Timbuktu was regaled as a place of great learning, where merchants made more money from the sale of books than any other merchandise. While the European Cainites considered the entire continent a land of chaos lacking in civility, Nosferatu emissaries spread tales of cities that remained hidden from the West. Broods bled the kine of Gao, Bilma, Axum, Dongola, Sijilmasa, Katanga, Khami, Kukwa and countless other cities inland that the Cainites of Europe never knew… and still do not know. As today, so was it then: The Nosferatu succeed wherever they remain unseen. This was our age of empires.

African Empires

Human civilization in Africa prospered wherever trade routes succeeded. The first major empire was Ghana, which grew from the fourth century to the 11th. From its capital at Kumbi Saleh, we watched the caravans head across the Sahara with gold, salt and slaves. The King of Ghana was renowned for his generosity, holding vast feasts for his visitors the likes of which they had never seen before. Clan Nosferatu has learned to extend such generosity to its own kind as well, welcoming those who have traveled great distances to trade stories and enjoy our hospitality.

Yes, I have mentioned trade in slaves. Although some human historians are loathe to admit it, slavery was practiced in Africa long before your American Civil War. Some revisionist historians are infuriated by this statement, but I know that it was an acceptable practice in many large empires. It was essential for supporting traveling *dyula* of African vampires. Nosferatu who fed from these herds had little objection to the practice. A rather grim interpretation of African history, but a fitting one.

Over 10 million human souls were transported out of Africa prior to the 19th century, and with them came curious Nosferatu wanting to see the domains of Europe as well. What they found was a clan cowering from its lessers, hiding in sewers and caves and drainage tunnels. What they found was a system of princes and primogen lording over our brothers and sisters. Many of these emissaries turned around and started the long journey back to the African kingdoms. No doubt, some of them told outrageous tales about the dangers of the "dark continent," if only to discourage the Cainites of Europe from finding out what a haven it was for us.

Camarilla vampires can speak for hours about France, England and Germany, but empires like Kanem-Bornu have become a part of forgotten history. Because the Nosferatu and Gangrel — the two clans strongest in that empire — do not have as much influence over vampiric society, such legends have been neglected in many histories. Yet this empire surrounding Lake Chad supported entire generations of vampires for over a thousand years, well into the 17th century. At one point, the greatest emperor of Kanem-Bornu, Mai Idris Alooma, ruled over more territory than England's Queen Elizabeth, watching over grasslands from Darfur to Hausaland, dispatching emissaries to Tripoli and Cairo and exchanging gifts with the Sultan of the Ottoman Empire. Yet to the Europeans, this empire remained hidden, a historical cipher.

The Camarilla waxed strong in the predominantly Christian nations, but its influence never spread far into the Middle East or south of the Sahara. Muslim Assamites were often demonized as threats to its stable society, and thus, Muslim Africa is rarely mentioned in the histories of our race. Yet two of the greatest empires that hosted broods of Nosferatu — the Mali Empire and the Songhai of Gao — thrived because of the strength of Islam. This common African religion helped unify vastly disparate cultures, forging stronger trade routes and cultural exchange. While there are certainly Muslim vampires in the Camarilla today, many of the sect's Nosferatu have become martyrs for their faith. Even your oldest legend, that of the Curse of Caine, holds little meaning for them.

I do not wish to present you with exhaustive tales of our past glory, but I shall also cite the example of the Mwanamutapa Empire, which endured for a thousand years without the exploitation of the Camarilla. Throughout the entire time, African Nosferatu stalked the Great Zimbabwe ruins. We did not do this by forcing princes to bow before us, using our influence to affect the growth of cities or dominating rulers to obey our whims. As was our wont, we did it by silently lurking in the shadows, feeding only enough to survive and eagerly trading for information with the vampires who arrived in foreign caravans.

The Fall of Empires

Much of this African history is vastly outside the experience of the Camarilla Nosferatu. For you, in Europe, the Convention of Thorns in Silchester, England was a crucial turning point in your history, but the *dyulamansa* of Africa — the outsiders of Clan Nosferatu, it would seem — never heard about the formation of the Camarilla until much later. Even European vampires had great difficulty making the long journey to the village of Thorns; there was no chance at all that any from our kingdoms would attend. We had no Inquisition to goad us into joining your society; in fact, many African cultures hold a great reverence for magic and the supernatural and thus had little reason to fear us.

Yet when the European traders first came to Africa, Camarilla vampires were quick to follow. The Portuguese arrived in the 15th century, wiping out the Mogadishu and Mombasa empires in their search for gold and ivory. And with them came the Spanish Ventrue, the Lasombra, the Camarilla Nosferatu and other "Kindred" asking for introductions to the princes of our domains and the primogen of our cities. This part of the history you have neglected to mention at all. The European Kindred were shocked to see how we conducted our affairs. The African Nosferatu, and the other Cainites of Africa, had no such traditions, and when you heard we were without the benefit of your great leadership, it was the beginning of the end.

The Dutch arrived in Africa in the late 17th century — 1652, to be precise — and the result was a struggle well known to the Camarilla of Europe. Just as the white-skinned kine wanted to conquer and exploit their dark-skinned brothers, our Kindred "friends" arrived, wanting to rule us and teach us their Traditions. They could not believe that the African Nosferatu had existed without their system of civilization for so long. They were amazed that there were Gangrel who did not know (or care) how to recite their lineage properly.

With the growth of European settlements, the Camarilla came, ready to "accept" us into their sect.

But we did not want to be like the Nosferatu of Europe. We did not want to lurk in sewers, to hide in rivers of filth, to feed off the poor and diseased, to disgust the "civilized" clans with our hideous appearances. We would have been content to remain hidden, but the Camarilla began to divide the territories of Africa into domains. The Tremere chose a pontifex who had never seen the continent to watch over African chantries that had not yet been formed. Our Kindred spoke of developing trade and industry, battened on the slave trade, and began carving out Camarilla territories by sinking their claws into the autarkis who would not submit.

We fled further into the "dark heart" of Africa, but by then, you were determined to save us from ourselves. In the 19th century, Europe sent explorers to "discover" the wonders of our world. Curiously enough, the fact that there were already people living in these places did not diminish the importance of their discoveries; by their reckoning, they discovered the Mountains of the Moon, Victoria Falls and the source of the Nile. Just as Christian missionaries tried to "save" reverent Muslims and civilized pagans, Camarilla vampires were eager to teach us the true stories of Caine and the Antediluvians and "save" us from our Cainite heresies.

The European powers, aided by your Camarilla, then began to lay claim to our lands, our kingdoms, our continent. By 1884, they were well underway to claiming every territory on the map. By 1920, every square mile except for Liberia, Ethiopia and a few portions of South Africa were under "colonial protection." It took decades for the countries they developed to become independent. By then, it was too late. The cities had princes to watch over our lands. Your history became the history of our clan, and the empires of Mwanamutapa and Ghana, of Kanem-Bornu and Songhai, became trivia — footnotes in history. Nineteenth-century historians — like your academician, Alexander Ruxard — were quick to dismiss the history of Africa as one of barbarism and chaos before the coming of the Europeans, before the African Nosferatu became the Camarilla's burden.

You wonder why so many Gangrel have left this Camarilla of yours? I do not find the idea so outrageous. I need only remember the glory of looking out upon untamed wilderness from the acropolis of Zimbabwe, of the full moon gloriously rising outside my cave in Mwanamutapa, of the roiling waters of the Congo embracing me as I slept, hidden from the sun. Once, the Nosferatu shared all these lands, with the Gangrel and the other autarkis of Africa. Now the domain that has hosted me with its hospitality tonight is hidden in darkness, watered with rivers of urine and feces.

Now I see what I have been forced to join, what all of the Nosferatu have been forced to join. A pack of elders huddled in the stench of the sewers, reciting their history as if they had any pride left in their souls. This is not the clan I knew. This is not the sect I choose to support. You began by asking why we are all cowering in this sewer tunnel tonight? It is not because we have chosen to do so; it is because we have been forced to do so by your elders. I mouth my lineage for the princes of your cities, I obey your Traditions as I travel from time to time, I even try to understand the deranged philosophy of your enemies, the Sabbat. Yet I am still filled with shame, and my history serves as a reminder of what Clan Nosferatu has become.

ANOTHER CONTINENT, ANOTHER HORROR STORY

A Brazilian Nosferatu concludes the evening's festivities:
THE MORE I STUDY THE NOSFERATU, THE MORE MYSTERIES I UNCOVER. Your stories about Africa just confirm that. Just when I think I've uncovered a definitive truth about our clan, one of us finds a link to a Nosferatu who's hidden himself even better than we have. The diversity of our clan is the biggest mystery of all. There are those among us who fear what they have become so much that they hide from everyone, including others of our kind. For all we know, some of them may be among us right now, watching and judging us for what we say. Sobering thought, isn't it?

No matter where we go, there we are. As our Bestial friend has observed, when the Sabbat first traveled to North America, they were alarmed to find there were already exotic varieties of Nosferatu hiding in the wilderness. As our anachronistic *dyulamansa* has commented, when the European Camarilla tried to help "civilize" the continent of Africa, they did not account for the African Nosferatu who had already developed their own civilization. Nosferatu himself was originally a hunter, and his descendants have gone out into the night unafraid of anything less monstrous than they are. Our clan is perhaps second only to the Gangrel in our love for the feral, untamed wild.

And as for me — shall I tell you briefly of my story? I am from Brazil, and I also know of Nosferatu who hid from the depredations of their brothers and sisters in the depths of the chaotic, "uncivilized" world. As amazing as it may seem, my ancestors lost their domains to Kindred and Cainites on the other side of the planet. The Camarilla remembers the year when it was formed; I remember the year 1494 and the Treaty of Tordesillas.

Diplomats acting on behalf of Portugal and Spain gathered to drink fine wine, flourish the ruffles of their collars and debate the future of the continent of South America. Emissaries of the two countries drew a line on a crude map (about 50 degrees west longitude), deciding that Portugal would get the eastern portion of the continent, while Spain would get the rest.

When the Camarilla and Sabbat heard news of this, they too were eager to divide this brave New World between their two sects. Granted, the Camarilla and Sabbat Cainites were generally not as civil toward each other, but they still set upon a similar plan. A few wealthy princes in Portugal invested heavily in settling the northern coast, while Spanish Sabbat used what influence they could to receive fresh reports of explorers from their herds of kine. After European explorers had laid the foundation for settlements in the aptly misnamed "New World," ambitious neonates would follow, helping to develop herds of kine for the next generation of Cainites.

The mortal history that followed is straightforward and very relevant to the point I am about to make. In 1498, Europeans first explored the interior of South America. Christopher Columbus — on his third voyage to the West — landed on near the mouth of the Orinoco River. A year later, Alonoso de Ojeda, a Spanish lieutenant working for the navigator Amerigo Vespucci — and God knows what other secret patron — landed on the northern coast. Although the European Kindred knew nothing of the Gangrel, Nosferatu and other vampires who were already hidden there, they chose princes and elders to divide the domains of a continent they had never seen. Many who started the dangerous journey across the Atlantic received their titles long before they set foot in their new domains.

At the edge of the map, explorers would place a legend: Here There Be Monsters. And sure enough, when transplanted neonates began to feed upon the mortal settlers, there were Nosferatu already there, hiding and waiting. As happened with so many other places in the world, more European explorers and merchants arrived — Francisco Pizarro in 1509, Jiminez de Quesada in 1538 and so on — and European vampires eager to claim new domains traveled in their wake. By the end of the 16th century, European settlers had laid the foundations of cities, and wealthy vampires used what influence they could to secure them.

The invaders' interest intensified after the discovery of veins of gold and silver deep beneath the earth. This fervor did not abate when they learned that distant relatives of our clan also burrowed under there. The Nosferatu of the South American continent had remained undisturbed until the kine, whether motivated by mortal or

unseen overlords, began to descend into the earth for what wealth they could find. At the same time, the indigenous population was decimated by European diseases; those that survived were often forced into servitude.

We didn't have the strength to resist the Camarilla or the Sabbat; we crawled deeper into our domains as our herds were enslaved or destroyed, but within a century, our territory was limited to the tunnels and sewers beneath the cities of the Camarilla and the Sabbat. Our legacy remained, as always, in slums, sewers and rivers of shit. You say you have chosen this fate, but I did not. We did not. Which leads me to wonder....

The Chamber of Horrors is Closing

...in the end, above ground you must have the Haves, pursuing pleasure and comfort and beauty, and below ground the Have-nots; the Workers getting continually adapted to the conditions of their labour.

— H.G. Wells, *The Time Machine*

By your standards, we were autarkis: unorganized vampires who refused to accede to the European invaders. Yet I wonder what would have happened if these outcasts actually got organized? They failed to do so then, but what if they did so today? You say that the autarkis are welcome among the Nosferatu, but you do not act in this manner. The Nosferatu were powerless to oppose your two sects spreading into Africa, into Arabia, into South America, into the so-called New World. Our culture was never your culture, yet with the support of your allies above ground, you forced us to submit.

My colleagues, you were astute to notice that our autarkis friend, who seemed to have such a hatred for *The Book of Nod*, has disappeared from the room. He is a coward. My friends, you are perhaps surprised to hear our African colleague regale us with stories of kingdoms the Nosferatu once supported... and the Camarilla destroyed. My enemies, you can tell I carry little respect for the two sects you so religiously uphold, and you are perhaps surprised to see a third autarkis in your midst. You may be wondering: Are there more here tonight?

Listen very closely to the sounds in the tunnels surrounding you.

We have been hiding throughout the world. We have been, and we shall be again. You fear the Nictuku, but I tell you: You should fear us more. Or perhaps... *we have already begun to work with them.* Listen to the groaning of the ceiling. There! Can you hear the supports giving way? You feel the urge to flee, perhaps, yes? Do not bother. Do not bother triggering the explosive charges you have set up along the tunnels. They have already been disarmed. Do not bother running. You are already surrounded.

Our evening of stories has come to an end. I hope that you are swift, for at least one of you must survive and remember. The legends of our clan... all the legends of our clan... must live on, passed from sire to childe. Tell the story of this warren, and remember....

Our last storyteller vanishes. Fade to black, and *exuent omnes*.

Chapter Two: Inside Clan Nosferatu

"I am not a human being! I am an animal!"
— The Penguin, *Batman Returns*

Here's a little experiment: Go out into the woods, far from any trace of human habitation, and look under a rock. Once you're far away from the sounds of traffic and the sight of telephone lines, peek under a log, or, even better, flip over a dead animal with a stick. The little wriggly things you'll find underneath will tend to go in one of two directions: *up* or *down*. Disturbing little nasties squirm up into the light, but the truly horrid things turn around and dig deeper.

Uncovering the truth behind Nosferatu society is rather like picking up that rock. Other vampires have a very distorted interpretation of the clan. They've seen what oozes up to the surface, wriggling into their convocations, *ritae* and observances. They've witnessed what rises from the sewers to skulk in the shadows of the nearest nightclub or the prince's audience chamber. The Nosferatu, however, know that there are plenty of monstrous abominations that *never* rise to the surface. To track them down, we'll have to turn away from what you've been watching with disgust so far... and dig a little deeper.

Let the other vampires play at being *almost* human. Sabbat Creeps, Camarilla Sewer Rats, those stinky guys over in the corner — no matter what you call them, the Nosferatu have distanced themselves as far as possible from the human race. Other vampires can walk among mortals freely at night, pretending to remain within human society, but the Nosferatu exist further outside of it than any other clan. Although they must occasionally disguise themselves as humans to survive, Nosferatu have no need to emulate human culture. Instead, they've cultivated their own culture, one uniquely alien. It's spread like a fungus through the cities of the world, and like any really hardy mold, it thrives best where it can't be seen.

Nosferatu exist in two worlds: the world above and the world below. Above ground, other vampires try to ensnare them in either the treacherous politics of the Camarilla or the ruthless competition of the Sabbat. Below ground, other Nosferatu speak of their kind as the most fraternal of the clans. They must all work together in order to survive, it is said, and thus, many impress upon their own kind their "obligations" to their clan — or, more precisely, one of the broods of Nosferatu that claims to act on the clan's behalf.

There is a price for the power of Nosferatu's Blood and his "gift" of immortality. Being trapped in the guise of a monster for all eternity is just the beginning. The ugliness of a Nosferatu isn't just skin deep — so far, you've probably only seen the *attractive* side of the clan.

You can look at the surface of their society, if you like, guessing what you can from the rumblings, bubblings and gaseous emissions you hear deep within. However, if you wish to truly immerse yourself in the role of one of these monsters, you must cast aside appearances and discover what's roiling in the belly of the beast. Let's cut the clan wide open — with surgical precision, if you like — and see what we can find *inside Clan Nosferatu*.

THE NOSFERATU'S CHOSEN

A Nosferatu's foulness develops long before his Embrace. One of the most important decisions a vampire makes during his immortal existence is the selection of his childer. Indeed, it can be argued that no two humans receive the Embrace for precisely the same reason, though the vampires of each clan display a few shared preferences. The Chosen — humans ideally suited to the curse of vampirism — often reflect their sires in some way: in temperament, in psychology or in traits the sire admires. Thus, a childe can be seen as a mirror to her sire. In the case of Nosferatu, it is a very disturbing image indeed.

For the Sewer Rats, the most common characteristic shared among would-be childer is their alienation from human society. Even in life, Nosferatu Chosen are often physically, emotionally or psychologically scarred. Derelicts, the deformed, the autistic, the hopelessly antisocial and the criminally insane are all "attractive" candidates for the Embrace. There are practical reasons for this: Most humans do not have the fortitude to survive the transformation that results. Those who do must face contempt and isolation, sometimes for decades or even centuries at a time. Humans who have already endured lives of pain and suffering, on the other hand, are more likely to survive the ordeal.

Fawning petitioners to the Nosferatu flatter them with lies, but Sewer Rats know the contempt in which they're held. Such creatures are shunned, even among their own kind. If a human is chosen to endure immortality with a face like a train wreck, an aroma cultivated in the deepest realms of the city sewers and a reputation even vermin would condemn, social sophistication is not a top priority. Romantic vampires may fool their victims into "choosing" the Embrace themselves, but Nosferatu rarely have this privilege. Pity, mercy, disgust or outright loathing are all typical motivations for turning a human into a Creep or a Sewer Rat.

Sometimes a sire chooses poorly. The transformation from human to monster is an arduous one. The torment can kill the victim, corrupt his soul or simply drive him insane. If this happens, his sire may simply abandon the childe in the worst part of town and scurry off to another city, leaving the poor bastard to suffer. Few princes have the resources to track down every "illegitimate" fledgling vampire skulking in the city sewers. Again, there are horrid little things that never rise to the surface.

In Sabbat-held cities, flawed childer may be given a chance to survive their Creation Rites, but a sire can usually think of more practical ideas for what to do with them. For a start, rejected childer make excellent shock troops for crusades: Just drop them off in a Camarilla city, and their grotesque behavior usually strains the Masquerade right away. Rejected Nosferatu are also routinely recruited for Sabbat fun and games — a really callous sire can make a whole evening out of slaying his childe.

As one might expect, there is an alternative to dredging the scum of human society for suitable candidates. Embracing a human who is actually attractive, popular or prosperous is one of the cruelest punishments a sire can inflict. Since vampirism is a curse, the Embrace may be performed for vindictive reasons, giving a would-be childe "a lesson he'll never forget." Neglecting to teach these victims the art of Obfuscate can force them to suffer even more. The vain, the callous, the prideful — all are suitable recipients of Caine's curse. While the most horrid examples go irrevocably, suicidally and delightfully mad, the few who survive may actually benefit from the experience. Formerly beautiful victims learn quickly not to judge anything based on its appearance — one of the most important lessons a neonate can learn when dealing with this clan.

Personal experience and professional skill are two other excellent reasons for enfolding someone in the Embrace. With the resources Nosferatu have at their disposal, there's always a need for architects and engineers who can help expand a city's sewers, computer hackers who can gather information efficiently and illegally or career criminals who prefer to practice their trade in secret. Some sewer dwellers choose their childer hoping to create an empire beneath the city, gathering skills they think will be useful in their underground utopias. Broods of Nosferatu are often founded on such idealism.

Unfortunately, such schemes don't always work. There is no guarantee that any victims Embraced into the clan will immediately serve their sires' goals. Theoretically, blood bonds and brainwashing can ensure a childe will lend his skill to his sire's demands for a while, but abused childer eventually rebel, finding a place that suits their own strange desires. For all the talk of clan unity, Nosferatu rarely force others of their kind to do anything. Existence is horrific enough without needing to emulate the treachery of the other clans.

An intelligent, cunning and resourceful Nosferatu can find a niche in just about any city in the civilized world. The Camarilla and the Sabbat eagerly accept vampires who are well practiced in performing their tasks unseen. As long as the Nosferatu keep upwind from the rest of the sect, the others don't look too closely at what the Sewer Rats have unearthed.

THE EMBRACE

The Nosferatu Embrace is a slow and agonizing experience, a monstrous transformation from a human being into a monster of an entirely different species. Other vampires may think that maintaining a human form and walking among mortals helps them preserve their humanity. The Nosferatu hold to no such pretense. Of all the species of vampires, the Nosferatu are unquestionably the most alien, and a Nosferatu's Embrace reinforces that mindset. Let the Toreador and Ventrue pretend to be blessed with immortality by their sires; the Nosferatu are far more likely to think of vampirism as a curse.

It begins with a Kiss: in this case, complete exsanguination. After a human victim has been drained of all its blood, one toxic drop of Nosferatu vitae is enough to pollute the entire body. The transformation takes almost a week to complete or even longer if the change is especially severe. As the body enters the first stages of living death, organs shrivel and veins harden. Any human blood ingested quickly transforms into a thick, bilious fluid — one tainted as much by the Curse of Caine as by an abundance of genetic waste. Constant pain twists the once-human face into a perpetual grimace, creating constant agony. The only sensation that can block out this torment is an overwhelming thirst for human blood.

Within a matter of days, dead skin becomes coarse and stretches tightly across withering muscles. Old organs distend into sacs for storing vitae. The bruises endemic to rigor mortis develop on the flesh. Hair falls out in patches. The cartilage of the nose and ears collapse or distend. In some cases, the childe may adopt certain "signature deformities" of his sire as the hereditary curse is passed to the childe — not unlike, some scholars opine, the inheritance of original sin — but there is no guarantee what may befall a Nosferatu's childe.

A kind Nosferatu will tend to his childe like a feverish patient, watching the transformation with loving care and placing fresh blood for the victim to ingest. Such kindness is exceedingly rare. Cruel Sewer Rats record the experience on film or video, surround the childe with dozens of reflections of his new hideous form, lecture the childe on the reasons for his punishment or simply bury the victim to await his "rebirth."

While other vampires may speculate why the line separating Camarilla Sewer Rats from Sabbat Creeps is so waveringly thin, Nosferatu already know the most obvious one: The Creation Rites of the Sabbat are rarely more torturous than a Nosferatu's Embrace.

By the end of the week, the victim's very bones gnarl and warp. Any lingering similarity to human guise is vague at best. The resulting creature is no longer human — it is an entirely different species, divorced of mortal concerns. During the last stage of transformation, the skull assumes its final shape, elongating, flattening or caving in entirely. Many humans associate their face with their identity; this falsehood is the last thing to crumble during the metamorphosis. A fledgling vampire's dead organs may twitch and shiver for weeks afterward while adjusting to the newly found form, but by then, the personal horror of utter alteration is complete.

Not everyone survives this cruel process. The most horrific changes occur not to the body but to the victim's mind, inflicting such pain that they force a victim to the very limits of his fragile sanity. Weaker minds become even more monstrous than the bodies they inhabit. Such creatures become mindless brutes — in Camarilla society, it is a sire's duty to hunt down and destroy such abominations.

Sabbat vampires entertain the hope of reforming such wayward childer, subjecting them to further Creation Rites. The most monstrous creatures of all remain autarkis, skulking outside the boundaries of both Camarilla and Sabbat society. These socially amoral failures then exact their rage upon human victims with wild abandon; spreading their suffering to others is only act that can give their damned eternity meaning. Camarilla convocations host the "saints" of Nosferatu society, the ones that endlessly reflect upon their sins, but far more sinister creatures remain in the shadows, hidden from the eyes of Camarilla and Sabbat vampires alike.

THE THOUSAND FORMS OF FLESH

Flesh is weak; only by will may it be made strong. Some outsiders to Nosferatu society repeat clichés about Sewer Rats being "the most humane of vampires, despite their foul appearances." In truth, Camarilla Nosferatu who learn to interact with the other five clans are just the most pleasant ones. They are but a brief glimpse of their Antediluvian's eternal curse. No matter how much a Creep or Sewer Rat suffers, he's probably seen others who've had it much worse. The underworlds of major cities are often haunted by vampires too grotesque or uncivilized to interact with the world above.

If a Nosferatu decides to maintain his humanity, it is because he has no doubt seen the alternative: an inexorable descent into utter abomination. Nosferatu can see their own ugliness quite clearly, both inside and out. By admitting how horrible they really are, many are able to escape the descent into truly monstrous behavior. The deeper one travels into the sewers, of course, the nastier the aroma gets. Hold your nose. We're diving in to see what we can find.

MARTYRS

The Embrace ends a victim's life, tears him away from his friends and family, drastically alters his appearance and identity and, worst of all, forces him to watch the entire process. Humans sometimes say that suffering is good for the soul: If it is, then anyone who can survive the Embrace is a candidate for sainthood. A neonate Nosferatu who can avoid sinking to the depths of depravity must have something very strong in his psyche — sometimes it is nothing more than a noble cause or belief. Victims who manage to retain their human morality despite centuries of torment often come to consider their fate a punishment for the sins of their former lives; thus, other Nosferatu commonly refer to them as Martyrs.

By silently watching humanity from the shadows, Martyrs make a careful study of the human condition. To distract themselves from the horror of what they have become, they remain fascinated with humanity: human morals, human ethics and human failings. The most extreme watch over the weak, protect the innocent or punish the unrighteous. Such efforts aren't always fated to succeed, though; a Martyr, for all his fascination with the human world, is still a monster. No matter how careful he is, he may eventually slip up and fall prey to the Beast that dwells within his soul. He may even end up victimizing or feeding from the very humans he wants to protect.

Martyrs are not easily fooled by appearances: After all, in human society, the most attractive mortals can also be the most decadent or degenerate. Martyred Nosferatu have a keen eye for moral failings in others and, despite their prudish behavior, are drawn toward finding it. The advisor hovering near the prince's chambers, the crusader condemning the latest Sabbat crusade, the Noddist whispering rumors of Golconda — all of these creatures rationalize their activities by claiming to be martyrs to a cause.

While a neonate Nosferatu of this type may be responsible for some of the most revolutionary changes in vampiric society, he may also be known as a simpering, obsequious, smelly, unwholesome pain in the ass.

Crude or bestial Nosferatu would just as soon flush them back from where they came. If a Martyr can remain true to his beliefs, however, he is worthy of great respect from vampires of any clan. Many of the most esteemed Nosferatu of vampiric history are martyrs for their beliefs; their histories reflect centuries of nobility, sacrifice and, ironically enough, humanity.

CLEOPATRAS

Beauty's only skin deep, but ugliness goes much deeper. While some Nosferatu struggle to remain humane, not all of them succeed. Their cursed state often spawns a festering hatred for all things beautiful. This resentment grows especially strong in Nosferatu who deal with Toreador and Tzimisce vampires, who often use the power of the Blood to achieve unearthly beauty. "Beautiful People" become these Nosferatu's most hated enemies after the Embrace. Many Kindred can remember stories of mass-murders at beauty pageants, rampages in art galleries and other acts of revenge perpetrated by outraged Nosferatu. Yet even these extremes cannot compare to the most satisfying form of poetic justice: finding a beautiful, happy person and subjecting her to the horrors of a Nosferatu's Embrace.

Few sounds soothe the Beast like the screams of a beautiful creature in pain, the agonizing wail of a former Narcissus who realizes he's been transformed into a hideous monster. Younger Nosferatu refer to such a victim as a "Cleopatra." The name does not come from the annals of history, but from a more appropriate source: a classic film called *Freaks*. Cleopatra was a cinematic beauty, a vain trapeze artist who was grossly disfigured at the end of the film, when she was finally brought into the freaks' dysfunctional and alien world.

Vain, petty humans usually snap under the strain of the metamorphosis, going irrevocably insane. Those who avoid suicide or self-destruction actually may be redeemed, becoming productive members of vampiric society. A few have actually recovered their humanity in the process, learning that their identity is shaped by more than mere appearance. Many do not — instead, they plead to learn to master the Discipline Mask of a Thousand Faces as quickly as possible. Once they are able to change their appearance, they use the same tactics of manipulation they cultivated while they were alive. "Beauty is truth," the poets opine, "and truth is beauty," but for a jaded Cleopatra, immortality offers a chance to see the lies that lurk behind mere appearances.

FETID LITTLE CREATURES

Not every creature corrupted with Nosferatu blood survives the transformation that results. Some victims endure such severe changes that they cannot even pretend to be vaguely human afterward. The skeleton may erode; the eyes may wither; the arms and legs may warp to such an extreme that the resultant horror cannot even stand. As one might suspect, such abortive attempts at the Embrace are rarely introduced to the local Camarilla prince. Miserable wretches who shouldn't survive the Embrace are usually destroyed by their creators... usually, not always. Maternal instincts and fatherly love have been known to illicit sympathy for even the most abominable childer.

Freakishly fetid little creatures are sometimes nursed on blood and kept in a state of eternal death, if only to wallow in the filth of the local sewers. Such undead abortions are rarely given names, though they may find a home in a Canopic jar, a pool of bloodied water or a comfortable septic tank. It is common for them to die within the first few weeks after the Embrace, but the unfortunate few that survive remain hidden, unnoticed by even the rest of vampiric society.

FAGINS

Does physical degeneracy spawn moral decay? Just because someone's ugly, does that mean he's corrupt? One of the most distasteful types of Nosferatu is the beast whose criminal attitudes are as twisted as his appearance. Sewer Rats have an attraction to the unsightly and horrific, and they sometimes recruit victims whose morals are the most disgusting aspect of their personality. Morally degenerate Nosferatu often develop blood cults of amoral servitors, fanatics who would risk their lives for one more taste of tainted vitae. A blood-addicted ghoul would do just about anything to help its master extend his influence in the underworld.

In the Victorian Age, beasts of this sort were known as Fagins, named for the infamous villain in *Oliver Twist* who ensnared orphans in his web of crime. Victorian London once harbored "thieves' citadels" where criminal gangs would hide in squalor; modern Fagins make their home in abandoned buildings or slum tenements. Criminal Nosferatu have no need of sewers; they thrive above ground in the "bad part of town," surrounding themselves with human pawns. As long as they serve his will, he'll use and discard them as he sees fit.

By recruiting a gang of ghouls, Fagins learn to exploit the desperate, the disadvantaged and the simply deplorable, thriving in a very different sort of "underworld." They often have a certain theme to their cults: While one may string along a group of drug addicts, another may prefer transient spies, street kids or even prostitutes. Sewers may be useful for traveling unseen from one side of town to the other, but Fagins are just as comfortable in squalid, decaying neighborhoods above ground. Street-savvy and sinister, they specialize in learning to pick up the "word on the street," no matter how reprehensible or foul that language may be.

LEATHERFACES

A few Nosferatu are so disturbed by their Embrace that they adapt fully to become absolutely inhuman. All vampires prey on humans, but disturbed Nosferatu like to play with their food, often by hacking it into tasty bite-sized chunks. In homage to the mutilated serial killer of Tobe Hooper's *The Texas Chainsaw Massacre*, a killer of this kind is often known as a Leatherface.

This type of creature either inherits its hatred of human beings from its sire or develops murderous impulses after a particularly grisly Embrace. A Leatherface is a predator, an enemy of mankind, a serial killer or mass murderer in the guise of an immortal monster. It is no longer human — instead, it's moved up to the top of the food chain. Most learn from the masters: watching slasher films, studying killers with high body counts and stalking suspected criminals are all useful training techniques. Why pretend to be human? It's far more fun to wade through a sea of bodies and blood.

Nosferatu killers learn to maim and murder with the most savage, brutal weapons available. The tools of the Leatherface's trade are well known to film buffs: the ice pick, the chain saw, the power drill and so on. Hunting often gets particularly messy. A Leatherface likes to stage every aspect of the experience just right, employing all the tricks of the craft: the rickety staircase in the basement, the lonely stretch of woods or the trap that will trip his victim while she's running away. Cinematic clichés are a Leatherface's bread and butter (or blood pudding, as the case may be).

While Martyrs are fascinated with the kindest and most civilized humans, Leatherfaces are intimately familiar with the most degenerate examples of humankind. The Leatherfaces' morality cannot be defined in human terms; after all, deliberate murder ranks very low on the Hierarchy of Sins, preventing Leatherfaces from surviving the Path of Humanity for long. They can rarely endure the strict morality of the Camarilla, but then again, they are often far too independent to side with

LEATHERFACES AND SPLIT PERSONALITIES

The most contemptible variety of Leatherface not only hides his crimes from other vampires, but from himself as well. By rationalizing away his actions, actively denying his baser instincts and concealing a split personality, he can completely infiltrate Camarilla society without being aware of his own crimes. Beneath a pretense of martyrdom and humanity, Camarilla Leatherfaces slowly click off a body count any mass murderer would envy.

If the Storyteller allows this type of character, he may decide to let the Nosferatu hide his "extra-curricular" activities from the other members of the coterie and himself. The Derangement Split Personality works beautifully for this purpose. While the *player* is aware that a Camarilla Leatherface has a low Humanity or Path Rating, the character is completely unsuspecting.

the Sabbat. They are most typically autarkis, rejecting all politics to further their own, very personal goals.

Humane Nosferatu, especially within the Camarilla, consider Leatherfaces a disgrace to their own kind, monsters that threaten the Masquerade and the survival of all Nosferatu. When evidence points to a Leatherface crashing into a Camarilla fiefdom, local Nosferatu may decide to band together to swiftly eliminate this beast or at least lead the chase in destroying it. Sabbat vampires, on the other hand, are eager to use these beasts as shock troops in their crusades. Although discretion prevents them from ever offering these creatures a home in a Sabbat-held city — even the Sword of Caine has to be discreet enough to survive — Sabbat Creeps marvel at such ruthlessly efficient killing machines.

BESTIALS

Once a Nosferatu's metamorphosis is complete, he may decide to hide his face from society, vampiric or otherwise. Until the creature is ready to emerge from the shadows again, he may prefer the company of vermin, insects or animals to what presumably is his "own kind." Nosferatu refer to these reclusive hermits as Bestials. When cornered and provoked, Bestials have been known to insist that they are not human anymore, merely animals of the basest variety. This self-pitying indulgence may last for decades or even centuries before the feral, skulking monster rises from the depths of the sewers to attempt interacting with its own kind again.

As one would expect, Bestials are masters of the Animalism Discipline and inspire loyalty in the swarms

that follow them. Even after they ally with other vampiric conspiracies, they still tend to their swarms of rats, hives of insects, packs of dogs or clutches of reptiles. They communicate in grunts, groans, wheezes, gestures and obscene gaseous emissions, sometimes because they have lost the capability for human speech. Picture a child raised by rats or alligators, perpetually surrounded by roiling, turgid rivers of shit. Bestials who are paranoid about legendary Nictuku build vast swarms to defend their favorite sleeping chambers.

When necessary, Bestials learn to interact with the world above ground by sending out animal messengers. The Animalism Discipline is essential to a Bestial's survival, as it allows them to use various animals as their eyes and ears in the world above. It is, however, terribly addictive. Indulging too often jeopardizes their survival; it's better to stay in one's true form, no matter how unpleasant it may be.

Bestials' presence slowly alters the temperament of their favorite creatures. Blood-addled animals weaned on Nosferatu vitae sometimes develop a hatred for humanity that mirrors the misanthropy of their masters. Most animals will not confront or harm humans unless they absolutely must, since violent behavior jeopardizes their survival. Animals who have prolonged exposure

to a Bestial's crude applications of the Animalism Discipline, on the other hand, cannot conceal their venomous disposition and are eager to make humans suffer as much as possible. For this reason, a Bestial cannot stay in one domain for too long; after a few years, incidents of violence will betray his presence. If the Bestial gives into temptation and creates a thriving spawning pool of animal servants, his critters' appearance will be as abhorrent as their shocking behavior.

Bestials can't hide forever, of course. Some learn inner strength from their years of isolation and eventually decide to rise to the surface world. Since they like to surround themselves with other creatures, Bestials prefer to find a coterie or pack they can trust. Unfortunately, no matter how civil they try to be, Bestials can remain slightly feral for decades after they return to the world of the unliving. They revel in acting like monsters — they are more beasts than men.

On the rare occasions that Bestials are sighted, other Kindred recoil at their obvious flaws. Reptilian skin, clawed paws, alligator mouths and four-legged gaits are all common deformities. Those that can walk on two legs are sometimes entrusted with patrolling the more remote realms of a Nosferatu kingdom, tending to the beasts that spawn there. Others remain beneath the Earth, surfacing only to feed and watching the world above through the dark-adapted eyes of a thousand skulking beasts.

SKINS

The opposite of Bestials, these Nosferatu prefer the Discipline of Obfuscate and all the supernatural disguises that come with it. Their immortality is based on a joke that never gets old: Humans are ugly on the inside and attractive on the outside, but there are worse monsters stalking among them in human form, mocking them in their midst. Nosferatu who specialize in impersonating humans are known among the clan as Skins. After developing an addiction to the Obfuscate Discipline, they become consummate actors, blending thoroughly with humans and using their own appearances against them. This places them on an even footing with other humans. Human monsters walk amongst mortals all the time... some are just better at disguising themselves than others.

While such creatures may appear on the surface to be the most humane, they're actually in the depths of denial, desperately trying to figure what they really are. Some cannot remember who they ever were. Many manufacture elaborate identities, impersonating elders, ducti, primogen or princes. Such elaborate façades are doomed to fail — it's only a matter of time before someone sees through the disguise and is horrified by the face beneath the flesh. Then again, many vampires are known for their elaborate self-destructive schemes, deliberating destroying their unhappy existences with epic, tragic failures. If a Sewer Rat tries to use his supernatural powers to overcome Nosferatu's curse, after all, he deserves what he gets.

Elder Nosferatu who can "spot the Skins" may recruit them as expendable allies, spies who get a little too wrapped up in the roles they play. Neonates often go through a phase where abusing Obfuscate is a common practice; they eventually learn to use it sparingly (or not at all). Those who never grow out of this phase slowly go insane, unable to differentiate their alternate personas from their true identity. In this way, no matter how pretty they make their illusory faces, Skins are some of the most hideous Nosferatu of all.

One of the common variants on this theme is the neonate vampire who prefers to remain hidden as long as possible, fooling himself into thinking he's "invisible." Like the Martyr, he tries to develop an objective view of human culture; like the Leatherface, he gets off on lurking near potential victims; but more than any other similarity, like any other Skin, he's assured that staying disguised in plain sight will help him survive. It will... but only so far. Obfuscated Nosferatu neonates forget that an observant vampire has ways to see through such disguises. Childer who succumb too readily to the easy way out — depending on Obfuscate all the time — eventually get caught one time to many, sometimes with fatal results.

While "invisible Skins" are particularly adept at gathering information — particularly for gathering whispered secrets from private conversations — they are just as expendable as fools who are too eager to don the Mask of a Thousand Faces. Neonates get a rush from being invisible, but the eldest Nosferatu learn to accept their curse, spending as much time as possible in monstrous forms. By eventually "shedding their skin," Nosferatu learn to be proud of the curse their founding Antediluvian granted them.

LOREMASTERS

The occult world is filled with mysteries and secrets. Few individuals can keep track of them all... save, perhaps, learned masters of lore. An average Nosferatu can gather a few choice tidbits about whom the prince has been bleeding lately or which junk bond appeals a little too much to the Ventrue primogen. Gathering such information on a routine basis appeals to neonates, but elders tire of wading through such muck over and over again. There's a much larger world outside the halls of the prince's meeting chamber, and Loremasters spend eternity studying as much of it as possible.

Other supernatural societies often fascinate Loremasters far more than their own. While each clan has vampires claiming to claim this coveted title, Tremere and Nosferatu are often the most suited to it. Elders fascinated by occult lore commonly recruit neonate coteries to help them research such subjects firsthand.

No matter where they get their information, Loremasters speculate in matters esoteric. Because their trade is so specialized, they may know only a few others who trade in the same information. Such tightly knit conspiracies of experts disregard all boundaries of clan and sect: If a Camarilla Tremere finds out some esoteric fact about the Cathayans, for instance, he won't forego the opportunity to trade secrets with a Sabbat Creep. These societies are also extremely insular, and the eldest members are cautious about trading outside the circle of conspirators they know.

To maintain their "edge," many Loremasters have been known to seed misinformation and misdirection in their accounts of other supernatural societies, passing them off as rumor and innuendo. One tidbit of information may be precisely correct, but if it's hidden in a morass of lies, it becomes somewhat incredible. Vampires outside this insular society expect Loremasters to fabricate stories just to spread confusion, making the truths they themselves hoard even more valuable. Thus, a neonate should never take anything a learned master of lore states at face value; only another Loremaster is really able to evaluate whether the facts are absolutely true or another elaborate hoax. For more details, check out *A Festering Heap of Game Mechanics* at the end of this chapter.

NOSFERATU CULTURE

Nosferatu culture spreads throughout a city like a disease, breeding in any place that's moist and damp. It's attracted to any dank, dark place where foul things flourish. Monstrous vampires skulk into sewers, trash heaps, abandoned buildings and hellish neighborhoods, drawn to realms that reflect their foul temperament. Since vampires don't need to breathe, Nosferatu can also hide under large bodies of water... or other fluids. They live in a world of their own, abandoning Camarilla or Sabbat society from time to time to stew and brood in their own fetid aroma.

Vampires of other clans may think that the Nosferatu have been forced to live in such horrific conditions because the other Cainites and Kindred have forced them out of the better parts of town. Untrue. Contempt, like respect, is a two-way street. Nosferatu are often just as disgusted with vampiric society as the local Kindred are with them. Arrogant princes, tedious Elysia and treacherous politics — why bother? The Nosferatu have their own domains, their own politics and their own culture. While many neonates spend a great deal of time in Camarilla society, they also have access to another world hidden beneath the cities of mankind.

Ironically, Clan Nosferatu, the most antisocial of the vampire clans, has also developed a strong sense of community. Ostracism from vampires and mortals alike has forced them toward a certain amount of cooperation. Like the misfits, fringe groups and outcasts of the human world, they find a certain amount of common ground, no matter what they may smell like. Let's scrape off a sample and see what we can find.

ANTISOCIAL SOCIETY

Other vampiric societies promote social behavior; Nosferatu society is based instead on decidedly *antisocial* behavior. Crudity is one of the most commonly displayed Nosferatu traits. After all, when you're utterly disgusted by your own appearance, there's not much reason to be polite about unsightly odors, smells, gases and vapors. Neonate Nosferatu delight in trying to gross each other out, holding epic contests precisely for that purpose. Sewer Rats in particular take pleasure in disgusting other vampires; if the local Camarilla has trouble tolerating them, they'll reciprocate by openly displaying their own brutish behavior, refusing to disguise who and what they

really are. Crude displays also serve as a great psychological weapon. Kindred are far more likely to betray their secrets after their composure has been shaken by a particularly stunning display of grotesquerie.

As remarkable as it may seem, however, while Nosferatu may celebrate flatulence and stench, they have also learned to cultivate many finer qualities. First and foremost, Nosferatu culture values honesty. An information trader who lies to his own kind can ruin his reputation, cutting himself off from all sources of intelligence. Hypocrisy is despised just as much — while vampires of other clans may try to present themselves as creatures of beauty, Nosferatu cannot hide the fact that they are monsters and often revel in shame.

Nosferatu honesty also includes a double standard. When dealing with vampires outside the Nosferatu's "society," lying becomes socially acceptable: It is a weapon to use against vampires of other clans. Misinformation is revenge against Kindred who have treated the Nosferatu poorly. As the saying goes, "you get with you pay for," and when other vampires reward the Nosferatu with treachery, providing dangerously misleading information is the best form of revenge.

Another hallmark of the clan is its legendary cynicism. Since Nosferatu are often outsiders to many of the Camarilla's activities, they often believe they have a very objective view of its failings. Even Nosferatu who are very actively involved in the activities of their sect tend to be grim realists. When you're used to looking at the world through a sewer grate, existence can become very bleak. Those who have become bitter over Nosferatu's curse tend to see flaws and failings in everything around them. Just as they won't hesitate to let everyone see their deformities, smell their aroma and witness their tragic fate, the average Nosferatu has little reason not to shock other vampires with something even more repulsive: the ugly truth.

Respect is the final and most critical element of Nosferatu culture. Kindred who scorn the Nosferatu should be treated with disdain; Cainites who treat them as equals are worthy of an edge in the information trade. Because Nosferatu are not easily fooled by appearances, if an obsequious petitioner of the clan is obviously fawning to get what he wants, he deserves a reciprocal amount of deception and deceit.

Among their own kind, Nosferatu particularly respect the elders of their clan and show their respect in a way that seems alien to many other vampires. Status and age are not social weapons used to bludgeon neonates into submission. Instead, neonates may choose whether to recognize the culture of Nosferatu society or reject it utterly. Those who refuse to recognize the wisdom of their elders can take their chances surviving without the support of their clan. Wise neonates, however, learn from those who have survived immortality for centuries; thus, prestige is earned, not forced. Existence is pain, and Nosferatu who have conquered the worst of it are worthy of respect. Elder Nosferatu are often seen as revered sages, but they are far from draconian leaders — eternity is bad enough without making it worse for the youngest vampires.

Solitaries

Cities that flourish support thriving, virulent Nosferatu communities based on respect and cooperation, but sadly, they are the exception, not the rule. Despite the best efforts of the Camarilla and the Sabbat, most cities simply don't have enough of a human population to support more than a handful of vampires. Only the largest cities are populous enough to support more than a few Nosferatu, and even then, there's no guarantee of a Nosferatu primogen bothering with local politics. The sewers are full of enough crap without adding on layers and layers of politics as well. While other clans may enjoy the prestige of appointing a local "elder" to represent all of his consanguineous brethren, most Sewer Rats just don't give a damn. You're better off on your own — and the most antisocial Nosferatu who espouse this opinion become known as "Solitaries."

Many Kindred praise the Camarilla as a complex, efficient and civilized society, but most Camarilla cities do not have more than one or two Nosferatu. Often, a solitary Nosferatu has the underworld all to himself. Solitaries in the smallest cities usually shun even their own kind, though they still interact with other vampires when necessary. Shambling horrors of this type trudge toward the sleaziest backwater burgs they can find, since these cities are the only places the Solitaries can contemplate their foul fate in absolute privacy. Solitaries are quite territorial about their domain and keep their contact with the rest of their sect as limited as possible.

There is one exception to this xenophobia: When Nosferatu from other cities come to exchange information, skulking Sewer Rats and solitary Creeps become models of decorum and hospitality, sparing no expense to impress their guests. This is not out of any pretense of civility — years of isolation leave them hungry for news from the outside world, news that can make the difference between comfortable isolation and sudden death at the talons of a supernatural threat.

J. Cobb • 2000

BROODS

If a city is large enough to support more than one Nosferatu, politics creep in like mold on week-old cheese. In the Camarilla, the Nosferatu don't hold formal gatherings to discuss their political diversions. Instead, they gather in loosely knit families known as *broods*. Because they're shunned by many other vampires, Nosferatu prefer the company of their own kind. Survival is also difficult for them — maintaining sewer systems, abandoned buildings and other hiding places often requires the assistance and influence of several vampires. Broods tend to form around a common goal, whether that's expanding a branch of the sewers, exploiting the humans of a local slum, building a killer computer network or thoroughly scrounging the city dump. No matter how you disguise it, Nosferatu society cannot survive without the help of its broods.

Interacting with other Nosferatu is never forced. Much to the delight of the other Camarilla clans, Clan Nosferatu does not hold worldwide convocations, national meetings or regional assimilations. Instead, they keep their business up close and personal... and far, far downwind from the rest of the sect. One brood's emissary may travel far to attend another brood's gathering, but he doesn't need to make a massive masquerade ball out of the whole event. Instead, information is carried from one brood to another like cancer spreading from cell to cell. Why gather all the Nosferatu in one place? The smell would be unbearable.

Of course, no Nosferatu is ever under any obligation to join a brood or even interact with the nearest one. If a Sewer Rat vastly prefers the company of his coterie to Nosferatu gatherings, he has the right to make that choice. If he wants to avoid other vampires entirely, the other skulkers must respect his wishes. As long as this lone Rat can gather all the important information he needs on his own, there's no real need for him to attend regular Camarilla functions. In addition, Nosferatu are remarkably apathetic about gaining "prestige" by making regular appearances at Camarilla events. Simply put, they have no real need to "see and be seen." If you are too ashamed of who you are to interact with others, the rest of Clan Nosferatu can certainly empathize.

A Nosferatu who does choose to ally with a brood places himself at the disposal of his brothers and sisters. If a member of a brood neglects to help out his underground relations, there's a price to pay. In any warren, there are a few (forgive the phrase) shit jobs that absolutely need to get done. The other members of the brood don't have the authority to "punish" recalcitrant members, but they excel at guilt-tripping, tormenting, harassing and insulting their so-called friends into pulling their own weight. Working with a brood doesn't prevent a Nosferatu from also joining a Camarilla coterie, but it does entail more work. As long as a Nosferatu's responsibilities are fulfilled — sometimes with the assistance of members of his coterie — the little Rat is encouraged to go out and gather more muck, rumor and innuendo with his chums.

Pooling resources can keep all the Nosferatu in a city from being left out to dry. Thanks to advances in technology, members of a brood can also actually decide never to see one another, but instead remain in "virtual" contact. Cell phones are a godsend to the Nosferatu; it's easier to have a ghoul hand one to a contact above ground than risk being seen by mortals. While tunnels have a bad habit of interfering with such conversations, a few resourceful Nosferatu have figured out the value of scoring influence in the communications industry.

Nosferatu hackers assembling in chat rooms, sewer crews constantly patrolling and maintaining their domains, slumlords exploiting the poor — no matter what tactic unites the Nosferatu of a brood, the same social mechanisms apply. Broods endure like dysfunctional little families, keeping gangs of Nosferatu allied no matter how repulsive their relations may be. While they may bicker and squabble, the vampires of a brood need each other... if only to practice disgusting one another.

COTERIES AND BROODS

Nosferatu characters, as they are commonly portrayed, exist in two worlds. Most belong to a coterie or pack — that is, a group of vampires from several different clans. Camarilla Nosferatu spend a fair amount of time consorting with other clans and even interact with them on a regular basis. Yet the Nosferatu also have many social functions removed from the rest of Camarilla society. A Nosferatu tends to feel pressure to place a local brood's concerns above the needs of his coterie — this conflict in a chronicle makes for excellent stories, drama and, above all else, roleplaying.

As an example, when a Camarilla city has more than one Nosferatu, the local Sewer Rats will want copious information on what the various coteries are doing. If a Nosferatu character wants to trade information, the first bit of gossip up for bid is usually what the other vampires of his coterie have been up to. A Nosferatu doesn't have to fall into this trap, but if the character takes the bait, he should be rewarded with all sorts of other facts gathered from the last Hosting. If the character refuses, he doesn't have to receive all the benefits the local brood has to offer. He can skulk in the sewers, but he shouldn't expect the clan to scurry to his

beck and call. Nosferatu who decide to share resources with broods tend to survive longer.

For Storytellers, there are several different ways to balance these two aspects of Nosferatu society. The Storyteller might decide to create a series of subplots based around a Sewer Rat's connections to his brood. The conflict between the (often exaggerated) pressures a vampire receives from his clan and the obligations he has to his allies can easily become a recurrent theme. An alternative involves making the local brood so beastly that a coterie's Nosferatu character would never get involved with it. A brood of Nosferatu may even serve as an excellent adversary, even if none of the characters are Camarilla Sewer Rats.

The final and most bizarre approach is running a "brood chronicle," where all of the characters in the coterie are Nosferatu. The Storyteller proposes a reason why all these Nosferatu would work together and then maps out a territory for them to muck around in. The obvious conflict in this type of chronicle involves contrasting the world above with the world below. Enough horrid things shamble underground to keep the brood busy for quite some time, but occasionally, the characters can rise to the surface world to trudge through

Camarilla or Sabbat politics. Emissaries from other broods, Nictuku sightings, Leatherface rampages and the like round out this approach to the game. The underworld is waiting — you get to decide how deep you want to venture within it.

Hostings

If the local broods and Solitaries really need to get organized, there are ways to scrounge them together. Any Sewer Rat can offer to sponsor a gathering to discuss the latest crisis in the city. When a swarm of Nosferatu all ooze into the same place, it's called a Hosting. The vampire who calls it is responsible for providing a time and place to meet, as well as the ambience such gatherings demand. As the monsters assemble, they regard each other with respect and gentility, showing a curiously high regard for hospitality. While other vampires may cynically regard this as affectation, it is quite sincere. Wading through shit is miserable enough; treating other Nosferatu like shit is simply unacceptable.

A Nosferatu may show up at another brood's Hosting with little or no advance warning and without any advance permission. If he's clever enough to find out where it is, he's worthy enough to attend. Invitations to Hostings — whether delivered by shambling messengers or on stained pieces of trash — are open to anyone who has the Nosferatu Antediluvian's vitae coursing through his veins.

On rare occasions, a Sabbat Nosferatu may attend a Hosting of Camarilla Nosferatu, or vice versa, though such meetings are performed with the utmost secrecy. Cooperation between different supernatural societies is often performed under the auspices of a temporary truce, and of course, such attempts don't always work. Aside from affiliations of clan and sect, individuals are wildly unpredictable — Nosferatu risking journeys to dangerous domains of alien Hostings take great risks. When these alliances succeed, however, the results are worth it.

Prestige

Each Camarilla clan has its own social mechanisms for keeping track of vampiric prestige. If you choose to spend eternity making existence easier for other undead, you deserve to be recognized for it. When one of the Kindred achieves a goal that impresses everyone, word quickly spreads throughout the clan of his success: That vampire gains Prestige, with a capital "P". When a vampire visits a city for the first time, there's a chance that the members of his clan will formally welcome him because of his accomplishments. In a society based upon social interaction, the phrase *"I know who you are"* goes a long way.

While the Camarilla is in part based on such vainglorious boasting, Nosferatu just don't get as worked up about it as many Toreador, Ventrue and Tremere do. Unlike most other clans, Nosferatu don't compete with their own kind to see who is the most esteemed. They don't slit each other's throats for social approval, they don't care who's wealthiest or the most beautiful, and they don't seek prestige for its own sake. As one would expect from a clan of shambling, hideous sewer-dwellers, egotism and vanity are not typical Nosferatu traits.

As one of the most unified clans, however, Clan Nosferatu does have many reasons to recognize its most prestigious members. Working for the good of the clan as a whole, creating something that makes the existence of all Nosferatu in a city more tolerable, expanding the local sewer systems and ensuring the survival of Nosferatu's descendants are all accomplishments worthy of recognition. Although Sewer Rats cannot force their own kind to work with the clan, survival often depends on cooperation; thus, working on behalf of the clan is not mandatory, but it is recognized and rewarded.

Actually accumulating accolades doesn't depend on age or political titles; unlike most other clans, Nosferatu don't award prestige to vampires just because they're old. However, Nosferatu are often recognized for surviving under adverse circumstances or fighting for causes they believe are just. A Martyr, for instance, who has held to his beliefs despite the scorn and censure of others for centuries is certain to gain the admiration of other vampires. Since no Nosferatu is able to *force* another one to obey, status itself is never forced or demanded, merely respected. Everyone's entitled to an opinion in a Nosferatu Hosting, but other vampires tend to listen most closely to the ones with the most prestige.

Unlike most of Camarilla society, Nosferatu elders don't lord over neonates just because of their status. As one would expect, when they shamble back to the rest of their sect, they retain this egalitarian attitude and don't fawn over the prince and elders just because they're the current "rulers." Strip away the pretense, the finery and the eternal posturing, and the appearance of power is revealed for what it really is. Strip away the attractive faces and a few layers of flesh, and what's left over is typically Nosferatu — pustulent, sore-ridden, diseased Nosferatu.

Sects and Politics

To outsiders, the vampires of Clan Nosferatu can be divided into three factions: Camarilla Sewer Rats, Sabbat Creeps and autarkis. The Sewer Rats are Nosferatu who formally introduce themselves to the prince of a Camarilla city and acknowledge his authority. The Creeps are Nosferatu who have undergone Creation Rites and formally serve the Sword of Caine. Autarkis vampires, of course, reject any political affiliation and don't really refer to themselves as any sort of gang, political faction, social club or philosophical organization. This very simplified view of Nosferatu society pleases most other vampires, who often break down all sorts of supernatural creatures into nice, broad categories.

It also pleases most Nosferatu, because... *it is a lie*. It is an utter and complete fabrication that misdirects anyone outside their society from understanding how the Nosferatu really work. Nosferatu are first and foremost individuals; political affiliation is just another delusion of the surface world. Generally speaking, Nosferatu care less about distinctions between vampiric sects than any other group of Kindred. When Nosferatu interact with other vampires, they nearly always request an exchange of information.

No dictum, tradition or treaty forbids Nosferatu of different sects from *talking* to each other. If the princes and archbishops are offended, then such exchanges must be conducted in secret... and, in fact, they are, regularly, between emissaries from different clutches, broods and Hostings. Of course, such exchanges involve risk. While Camarilla and Sabbat Nosferatu endure a tenuous truce when exchanging information, individual Nosferatu may have a fierce hatred for a particular sect. Survival also means adhering to the same philosophical beliefs as your allies — a Camarilla Martyr doesn't have to jeopardize his political position every time an anarch arrives in town asking for secrets about the local prince. Trading secrets is possible, but no Nosferatu ever trades foolishly.

OSTRACISM

Among the Nosferatu who consort with other clans, bloodlines and cultures of vampires, Camarilla Sewer Rats are the most common. Embracing the politics of this sect, unfortunately, means accepting censure, scorn and ostracism. Nosferatu are the red-haired, reptilian stepchildren of the Camarilla. They rarely volunteer for the most prestigious political titles, and they are rarely nominated for them. Many Camarilla vampires eschew the idea of inviting these mangy, smelly, obsequious bastards into the highest levels of political power. In fact, Nosferatu princes are almost unheard of — while there are a few Sewer Rat sheriffs or scourges within Europe and North America at any given time, they are more the exceptions than the rule. As one would expect, they must be exceptional in the performance of their duties.

The ostracism Nosferatu face from the other Camarilla clans isn't just the result of prejudice. Because of their common need for survival (and their common fear of the Nictuku), the Nosferatu have a strong information network and political presence of their own. If more Sewer Rats were to obtain positions of political power, their cultural ties would make them truly formidable. Imagine a prince who has spies stalking unseen among all the local coteries, Skins infiltrating the domain's conspiracies and invisible enforcers with titanic strength to back it up. Other Kindred only suspect what lurks beneath the asphalt of their cities, and fear of the unknown is always more powerful than prejudice toward the known.

Fortunately, the vast majority of Nosferatu have no desire to accumulate such obvious avenues to power. Princes, even among the undead, come and go; the strength of a brood of Nosferatu lies in its ability to remain unseen. Instead of scrounging for political office and the vainglorious prestige that comes with it, Nosferatu focus on building their information networks. Even a Solitary who shuns the confines of broods and Hostings can access a few choice secrets if he needs to (for a price, of course). Information is the Nosferatu's stock and trade, the common currency of their society. With each transaction, a Sewer Rat becomes more powerful, laughing up his sleeve at how thoroughly his race has infiltrated the Camarilla.

AUTARKIS NOSFERATU AND BELIEF

Becoming autarkis involves far more than simply rejecting the politics of the Camarilla and the Sabbat. Many autarkis Nosferatu reject the basic ideas on which both sects are based. These fundamental concepts are antithetical, in many ways, to a Nosferatu's existence.

To begin with, Nosferatu society is extremely egalitarian; while elder Nosferatu are revered for their wisdom, there is no need to obtain political status within the clan. No Nosferatu ever really forces another to do anything, since many would just as soon crawl into a dark hole and concentrate on simple survival. With this in mind, many Nosferatu don't see the need to prop up a Camarilla prince or Sabbat archbishop; the idea of recognizing the authority of other vampires seems alien. In the same way, autarkis vampires also see authority as a fabrication. While they aren't stupid enough to flout the Six Traditions in a Camarilla city, they feel no need to put themselves on a prince's leash and beg for respect.

Camarilla and Sabbat society are based on myths many autarkis refuse to accept. Both cultures entertain ideas that the Nosferatu were actually cursed by Caine, but a surprising number of autarkis refuse to accept the idea that Caine ever existed or at least question the details of such legends. According to these apostates, Caine is simply a legend meant to keep the Camarilla and Sabbat neonates in a state of perpetual fear. While several demented Ancients have stepped forward claiming to be the progenitor of all vampires, no one has actually ever seen Caine. As a myth, it attempts to define the vampire's place in God's universe, but many autarkis prefer to hold to their own religious beliefs or simply none at all.

Furthermore, while the threat of Gehenna has kept many neonate vampires fearful, autarkis see little reason to fear the rise of the Ancients. If the legends of the Nictuku are true, Nosferatu has already started killing his childer. Why, then, support any society that would have a philosophy for dealing with the End Times at all? The point is moot. Whether the Camarilla elders act as pawns of the Methuselahs or Sabbat packs stand a chance of rising up against the Antediluvians does not matter. Autarkis Nosferatu are prepared to accept the inevitable, much as they have accepted all the other ugly truths of their lives.

Apolitical, irreverent and isolationist — these are three of the strongest traits of the Nosferatu. Autarkis Nosferatu display all three qualities openly. They travel freely through the domains of princes and archbishops alike, stating their opinions to any broods who will hear them. This freedom of expression doesn't make them terribly popular, but then again, popularity is the least of an autarkis Nosferatu's concerns. Staying true to what you believe — no matter what the cost — is far more vital.

CREEPS AND SABBAT HUMANITY

As the cliché goes, Nosferatu are the most "humane" of vampires, even among the ranks of the Sabbat Creeps. Since they supposedly accept themselves as monsters, they have no need to indulge in shocking behavior. Masters of Obfuscate and misdirection, a Creep calculates his appearance precisely to attain the reaction he wants, whether that's fear, respect or pity. What lies within his heart, however, may differ completely from the façade.

Unfortunately, this statement cannot be applied universally to all Sabbat Nosferatu. As outcasts of both human and Cainite society, some of them choose to liberate themselves fully from conventional morality. What's the point of "accepting yourself as a monster" if your behavior is quintessentially human? Morality is dependent on the *individual*, not the sect; nowhere is this more true than among the Nosferatu. This is part of what allows Sabbat, Camarilla and autarkis Nosferatu to exchange information so freely: Political affiliation does not preclude communication.

Creeps value their individuality, almost to a fault. While the Vaulderie usually prevents them from placing the needs of a local brood or other Nosferatu above the needs of their own pack, Creeps are very secretive about their private activities. This is repulsive to many Sabbat, but Sabbat Nosferatu insist on the freedom to occasionally skulk off to pursue their own agendas. Beneath the calculated appearance, no one can guess what dark secrets reside in the withered hearts of these monsters. Thus, whether a Creep chooses to be humane or monstrous is ultimately his own personal decision.

ANARCHY AND MISINFORMATION

Among the ranks of the Nosferatu, a few are not content merely to hide from the political turmoil of Camarilla and Sabbat society — they want to tear it all down, destroying the hierarchy of princes, primogen, bishops and ducti and establishing domains where one vampire need never bow to another. This idea appeals particularly to neonate Nosferatu because it mirrors the hidden practices of the clan itself. Brujah anarchs often rebel against elders with little idea of what society to construct in their absence, but Nosferatu already have an working model of an alternative society.

Because of their talents for espionage, subterfuge and misdirection, a Nosferatu is an excellent recruit for any society of anarchs. Sewer Rats excel at finding out dirty little secrets and weaknesses of the city's elders, sometimes gathering them from Camarilla Nosferatu in

the same city. If such a nocturnal rebellion succeeds, the spy is certain to be rewarded... or pass on what's he's learned to the next group of rebels. If the rebellion fails, he may feel free to scurry off to the next domain, asking for sanctuary from another brood or at another Hosting.

THE WORLD ABOVE

Don't think for a moment that Nosferatu lurk solely in the local sewer system. Nosferatu who can imitate *anyone* through the use of the Obfuscate Discipline often prefer to make their home in the world above. Sewer Rats above ground often take credit for the urban squalor that sprawls across the largest cities. As parts of the city decay, the vampires of this clan extend their territories, reclaiming slums, abandoned buildings, industrial wastelands, homeless shelters and other urban nightmares as their domains. Urban eyesores reflect their attitudes toward the world. A rusting, abandoned building may serve perfectly as a massive middle finger raised toward the "beautiful people" of society.

As the city decays, the Nosferatu play. Elder Nosferatu use their diplomacy and influence, conspiring with fairer Kindred to keep a few neighborhoods "degentrified." Keeping the slums decayed benefits everyone in the clan, along with a few vampires outside it. It's good to have a few neighborhoods in town where the police rarely patrol. If a Nosferatu can break into someone's home without fear of police investigation, he can rip off anything he needs from the local kine. The Creeps of the Sabbat are masters of "urban renewal": If harpies get to take credit for art galleries and museums, it's only fair for Nosferatu to be proud of their status as immortal slumlords.

Vampires often regard humans as lesser creatures, and Nosferatu are no exception. No one is more beneath them than mortals trapped in the poorest and most impoverished parts of town. Preying off the dregs of society is very practical: The lower the station of a victim, the less likely others will believe he's been attacked by a monster. Creeps and Sewer Rats alike love to lurk among the city's homeless. A Nosferatu who spends a great deal of time stalking through the right neighborhoods can easily adapt them into his herds and feed off the with impunity.

Humans are easy prey, but they're especially vulnerable when they lack walls to protect them, others to defend them and laws that respect them. Transients are rarely accorded the same rights as ordinary citizens. They're treated as nuisances, harassed by police, swept from one neighborhood to the next and often purposefully ignored by the rest of their species.

If big cities aren't to one's liking, industrial wastelands outside the city limits are just as suitable. Nosferatu feel at home in neighborhoods that are as horrific as they are. Rusting, rotting, chemical-laden dumping grounds make them feel right at home. Because they aren't as susceptible to disease as humans, they're quite willing to move into abandoned buildings corrupted by toxic chemicals and waste. Some progressive Sewer Rats eschew such decadence and look to the future instead. They like to back new construction, trading favors to influence the creation of tacky, elaborate buildings. Nothing drives a harpy into a tizzy like a strip mall (or strip club) carefully positioned next to an artistic Elysium.

NOSFERATU GHOULS

Camarilla vampires never tire of boasting that they "control" human society. Nosferatu have no need to indulge in such arrogance. Instead, they carefully, swiftly and silently take control of the hidden power in a city, including the unseen servants who keep it running. Nosferatu routinely create ghouls to help them infiltrate human cities further... and exploit them for their own benefit.

Sewer Rats ignore human pawns in obvious places of power. Let the respected vampires muck about with mortal politics. Sometimes, 10 well-chosen bureaucrats or aldermen can achieve far more than the mayor ever could. Political celebrities come and go, but well-placed ghouls can stay involved in city politics for years and years. Corporate employees on the fast track to success may work for a company for a few years, but a janitor can gain access to the same building for a lifetime.

Anyone who wades through the detritus of the city — "sanitation engineers," janitors, street sweepers, maintenance workers and the like — scrounge for the Nosferatu what the more fashion-conscious clans leave behind. Many people ignore the workers who sort through their trash, blissfully throwing away what the Nosferatu harvest. They don't notice the construction workers toiling on skyscrapers far over their heads or, more importantly, the foreman who obediently follows his instructions for changes and alterations to the building's construction. Beneath the mortals' feet, workers scurry underground, performing unseen tasks, sometimes on epic projects the average citizen simply doesn't care about. Many of them are required to pass drug tests to keep their jobs, but even blood tests can't reveal an addiction to vitae.

Nosferatu also thoroughly dredge the lowest strata of society, recruiting humans who are desperate for power. Criminals, transients, drug addicts — such poor fools will do anything to improve their lot in life. Mortals trapped in bad neighborhoods, grueling dead-end jobs or debilitating cycles of addiction will occasionally cheat and steal just to get by. Imagine what they'd do for immortality.

Such opportunities are not without drawbacks. Humans who consume the blood of Nosferatu gain the same benefits as other ghouls: incredible strength, increased vitality and a reprieve from aging. Along with these gifts, however, they also receive a foul taste of Nosferatu's curse. After a thrall has taken the third dose of his regnant's blood, he begins to take on subtle changes that render him unattractive and unsightly. It's only a slight transformation, but mortals who deal with Nosferatu ghouls always suspect that something is not quite right with them. Acne, greasy hair, weight problems, slouching gaits and body odor are just part of the problem. There's an unnatural taint that goes deeper than pockmarked flesh. Over time, such minor flaws can become greatly exaggerated.

Animals are even better at noticing the genetic corruption in Nosferatu ghouls, reacting to them with fear and loathing. Any vampire with the Animalism Discipline can learn to calm down curious beasties, but creepy, tainted ghouls simply don't have this option. No matter how human they appear, the presence of Nosferatu ghouls makes cats caterwaul, dogs growl and all other animals go apeshit. More than one blood-addicted vitae-junkie has had to slay his own housepets to cover up his degeneration.

Because unseen Nosferatu regnants need many agents to act among the kine, they are unusually fond of developing blood cults. If they are too horrific to venture above ground, it's helpful to have many ghouls who aren't. Bitter Sewer Rats who loathe the thought of disguising their true appearance rejoice when an attractive ghoul reaches the third and final stage of her blood bond. They rejoice even more when she can bring her friends back to her master's crypt with her. A Nosferatu ghoul deep in thralldom must be very vigilant about gathering enough blood to sustain the cult; because regnants rarely venture into the waking world, the ghouls of a Nosferatu blood cult will sometimes sacrifice their friends and lovers to their master to sate their own addiction for vitae.

Blood cults are as rare as they are desirable, however, largely because they are so dangerous to control. To sustain enough ghouls for an effective cult, recruitment becomes essential. Sometimes this involves recruiting other Sewer Rats to help perpetuate the scam, resulting in entire broods based around the maintenance of elaborate cults. Despite reverential intentions, when a vampire's thrill of controlling others approaches mania, some Nosferatu cults become positively religious about protecting their unseen master. Like Leatherfaces renowned for breaching the Masquerade, Nosferatu blood cultists are sometimes slain as soon as they are discovered by a city's brood. The most successful cult leaders drift from town to town, leaving a trail of broken (and bloody) hearts behind them.

Kingdoms of the Underworld

Princes and cardinals claim to "rule" the cities of men above, but only out of ego, delusion and deceit. Want to hear a really great secret? No prince actually *rules* her city. No cardinal ever has complete *control* over his domain. He might have a great deal of political influence, but if other vampires recognize his political title or royal position, they are reacting to something that is purely illusory, a surface deception. No vampires are more aware of this than the Nosferatu, who do not succumb easily to surface appearances. They may openly acknowledge the authorities of princes and cardinals above ground, but once they skulk underground, they enter another world, one step further away from the delusions of Kindred and Cainite society. Rulers may pretend to command vampires in the world above, but Nosferatu command their own kingdoms in the underworld below.

Nosferatu kingdoms are as old as human civilization. From the first time the Nosferatu Antediluvian skulked into the nearest cave to hide from mortals, the clan has been creating its own hidden domains. The need to create realms where Sewer Rats and Creeps can walk in their true forms unites Clan Nosferatu more than any other force. Not all monstrous vampires can walk around with supernatural Obfuscate all the time. They need a place where they can stalk, skulk and brood undisturbed, even if it's deep, deep underground.

Since vampires have stalked the night in human cities since the dawn of human history, they have tried to influence the development of those cities for their own benefit. This is the only true way vampires can coexist with mortals, and Nosferatu know this well. Just as the archetypal Ventrue lays claim to the financial world or the stereotypical Toreador proclaims the cultural havens in the city as part of her domain, Nosferatu influence the development of the city's slums, barrens and storm sewers. In cities where the Nosferatu thrive, vast sections of the sewers are altered to accommodate their kind. Welcome to the Kingdom of the Nosferatu, a realm where monsters stalk freely, unafraid to show their true and terrifying forms.

THE MONSTER IN ITS LABYRINTH

All Nosferatu kingdoms lie at the center of vast urban labyrinths, sprawling networks of tunnels that form subterranean warrens. Underground domains have layers and layers of insidious defenses, sometimes more for the amusement of the local residents than for their actual safety. When a brood of Nosferatu infests a city, they immediately swarm to gain influence over the construction and transportation industries. Carefully chosen ghouls, political influence, blackmail and prestation are all essential to gain a stranglehold on the entrails of the city.

If Nosferatu broods have been working together in the sewers for a long time, they'll have twisted the bowels of the city to their own benefit. Elaborate tunnels are walled up, preserving the privacy of underground domains. Vast buildings are condemned, providing rotting husks of habitation for neonates. Stashes, caches and crypts contain hidden resources. Booby traps become more insidious as the warren grows — every sewer worker and transit cop instinctively learns that there are places in the darkness where they dare not venture.

Subway tunnels are another important part of a Nosferatu's labyrinth in many major cities. Not only do they provide rapid transportation and easy prey from late-night commuters, but they are powered by the city's electricity. It doesn't take much effort to siphon off enough juice from the tunnels to add to the warren's defense. Leading a few wires from the third rail to an electrical trap is even easier.

Over centuries, the greatest minds of Clan Nosferatu have devised ways to keep their kingdoms isolated and unseen. Consider that an elder vampire with a command of Protean may take the form of a rat or bat, crawling through spaces where no human can dare go. Some can even assume a gaseous form, wafting through pipes, vast vertical drops and cracks in walls. The oldest and most powerful Nosferatu can hide in niches deep beneath the city, deep within areas constructed centuries before the city's mortals were even born.

THE ANTECHAMBER

Just because your home is surrounded by piles of offal and excrement doesn't mean you can't entertain the occasional guest. Most Nosferatu warrens have an area that serves as a reception area and guard post, a network of rooms where visitors can be kept waiting while they enjoy the local ambience. Sewer Rats generally refer to this area as an Antechamber, although it is usually composed of several chambers, tunnels, corridors and dead ends. Weak vampires travel all over the

city to conduct their business, but when a Nosferatu has something valuable, anyone who wants to bargain with him should risk a descent into the local broods' underground empire.

The local Nosferatu like to keep this area as atmospheric and aromatic as possible. The Antechamber is designed to disorient visitors, both physically and psychologically. There is no short cut to get to this room; visitors get a circuitous tour on their way to meet the clan's elders. This is done partly out of practicality; after all, the local brood doesn't want visitors to learn the layout of its domain *too* well. More than any other instinct, this realm is maintained out of perversity. Nosferatu are made to suffer on the surface, so it's only right that those who visit them below should get the same treatment.

The Antechamber is designed with maximum paranoia, discomfort and confusion in mind. Tunnels are choked with sewage, filth and garbage, and visitors must often stoop, trudge or crawl on all fours to reach the inner sanctum. Masters of animals like to keep hordes of rats, roaches, bugs, slugs and other vermin nearby to entertain their guests. Petitioners who bitch and moan get led through a few more dead ends or are left to wait alone in the darkest, foulest areas of the labyrinth. Merciful Nosferatu steer their visitors away from the really lethal traps; vampires who are obviously trying to exploit their sewer-dwelling brethren don't get this privilege....

By the time visitors reach the center of the Antechamber, where their requests will be heard, they are physically disoriented and psychologically exhausted. The rare visitor who can endure this journey without complaint earns the respect of the Nosferatu. The analogy between the labyrinthine maze surrounding the Antechamber and the Byzantine politics practiced in the world above is obvious... especially to those who must suffer during their visits to either world.

THE CHAMBER OF HORRORS

Any thriving warren also needs an area large enough to hold all the freaks, Creeps and Sewer Rats within its territory. Nosferatu refer to this area as the Chamber of Horrors — it's a combination of an audience chamber, ballroom, recreation area and fallout shelter. The chamber is usually set in the most defensible area of the sewers. As one would expect, its name comes from the back room of a wax museum, where rubes pay a few extra shillings to see sights that chill their blood.

The decor of the Chamber of Horrors usually reflects the local brood's attitude to the outside world. Humane Kindred in prosperous cities maintain a chamber that makes their existence a little more pleasant.

Ornate tapestries showing the histories of local Kindred line the walls; crystal chandeliers wanly illuminate the interior; rows of sculptures stand stoically beside their Ancient owners. Martyrs thrive on cultivating an artistic ambience in such rooms; just as their tortured souls are trapped in husks of hideous flesh, they maintain beautiful inner sanctums in the bowels of the city sewers. Nosferatu visitors often get sick of such pretentious crap, but hospitality prevents them from expressing their opinions too freely to their hosts.

In particularly nasty cities, the chamber is a hellhole, a pustulent sore deep within the sphincter of the city. Monstrous broods create these rooms with shock value in mind. Grotesqueries of all kinds proliferate. Wax-museum effigies, implements of torture, elaborate displays of taxidermy, mummified corpses, glass jars filled with bloated human organs — you get the idea. Anguished Kindred put on a display of being horrified at a truly nauseating chamber, much to the delight of the local brood.

Security is tightest around the chamber, and as such, vampires who do not belong to Clan Nosferatu are never brought there. It is possible for a Nosferatu to sell information about the chamber's defenses, but only at the cost of his own reputation. Surrounding the Chamber of Horrors, traps, deformed ghouls, faithful beasties and other obstacles protect the safest area of the sewers. Only the local Nosferatu can remember where all the defenses are. As a last-ditch defense, clever Nosferatu keep track of which structural points to smash if they want to collapse the ceiling. If a brood is going to die, its members prefer to take their enemies with them.

Spawning Pools

The Chamber of Horrors lies at the heart of a brood's defenses; unspeakable abominations sluggishly crawl along the veins and arteries. Nosferatu share their domains with hosts of animals and insects, critters that slither and crawl where they please. The easiest way to cope with these infestations is to turn them to the local brood's advantage, usually through the use of a spawning pool.

In any brood's territory, elder Nosferatu share the duty of occasionally bloodying a local watering hole. This vitae-soaked cesspool attracts vermin who gorge themselves, developing a fierce addiction to vampiric blood, increased vitality and monstrous deformities. Spawning pools are essential to the maintenance of any underground kingdom, not only for pest control but also for defense. What human ghouls are to the world above, blood-addicted beasties are to the world below.

Spawning pools are usually created with one particular type of creature in mind. Insect hives, rat colonies and nests of cockroaches are all choice locations for tainting the local food, fluids and feces with vitae. Eventually, other sewer denizens begin feasting at the same spot, but by then, one dominant type of creature has usually claimed the spawning pool as its domain. Devouring the other critters who are drawn there is merely an added benefit.

Animals who feast regularly upon vitae develop the same addiction for vampiric blood that humans do, as well as the same devotion to their vampiric masters. As one would expect, it takes far less vitae to develop an emotional bond in a cockroach or fruit fly than it does in a lawyer or investment banker (though some would say not much more). Nosferatu may also choose to create spawning grounds for more exotic creatures, setting aside a pit or pond where the beasties must be cared for. Raising snakes or alligators takes a bit of work, but ultimately results in monstrosities whose strength and cunning makes up for the investment of blood. Nosferatu who dwell closer to the surface may instead develop an affinity for packs of feral dogs, kitty cats or even street kids. A bowl of vitae-soaked milk (or beer) can attract a host of thirsty friends.

V:tM System: If a horde of creatures feeds in a spawning pool, they do not all become full ghouls, but still develop increased Strength and Stamina (increase each of those Traits by one). They also degenerate even more than ghouled humans do: The glint fades from their eyes, their skeletons warp, and their temperament becomes vicious. Like full-blooded human ghouls, they can get testy if they don't get regular doses of vitae. Should this happen, they lock into a state of mind that approximates a vampire's frenzy. When the chance to feed approaches (say, when a small child sticks her hand down a sewer grate), the beastie needs to make a Willpower roll at difficulty 9 to avoid savaging its victim.

MET System: Any animal that feasts on blood from a spawning pool gains one extra Physical Trait; it technically also gains one Trait in each of the three Virtues. Prepare a few prop cards to represent these critters' statistics. If they are not fed at least once a week, the owner should make a Static Test for each one to see if it acts against the will of its owner and attempts to go completely feral; the Animal Ken Ability allows a retest.

LIVE-ACTION UNDERWORLD

While access to the local sewers is no longer automatically conferred on Nosferatu during character creation, a Storyteller may still wish to offer it as an enhancement to her chronicle. In some troupes, the presence of sewers is largely theoretical: A Sewer Rat who descends into the warrens is "off-site" for a few scenes, or he merely steps outside to have a chat with a visitor to the underworld. In others, particularly those

with a large game site or a number of Nosferatu, a physical location may become the sewers, such as a hallway, an isolated room or a basement.

Once a game location has been established for the warrens, the Storyteller should sit down with the Nosferatu players and map out what an intrepid explorer might see, what security measures have been taken by the Nosferatu, what places in the warrens are inaccessible except to Nosferatu or those guided by them, and are there any means by which an unaccompanied adventurer can avoid security or other hazards. Such maps need not be detailed down to the last brick, but having the major details noted and laid out can save arguments over what's supposed to be where, what trap should have caught which intruder, and the like.

Troupes who favor elaborate displays and set-building may let their imaginations run wild. If the Storyteller and Nosferatu agree to designate an area of the game site as the warrens, consider some decoration to change the ambiance from the regular game location (say, a fancy hotel ballroom) to the decidedly different Nosferatu kingdom. Dim lighting, plastic rats, sounds effects (such as dripping water or distant subway whistles) and the occasional extra touch (such as an inflatable gator if your warrens have spawning pools, an Antechamber set with old furniture and broken mirrors, the chamber of a closet Frank Sinatra fan) can go a long way to making the sewers more than a mere locational change. Storytellers may also wish to prepare index cards with descriptions and pictures of typical sewer hazards, along with the tests needed to defuse, spot or navigate them. If you choose to go this route, there should be a Narrator down below at all times, or at least within calling distance; you may find it helpful to request that any non-Nosferatu going into the sewers stop to inform the Storyteller, so he can send a Narrator below to run challenges.

GHOULS OF THE UNDERWORLD

When a Nosferatu makes a human his ghoul, there is a chance the subject may react rather poorly. Just as the Nosferatu Embrace utterly corrupts a fledgling vampire's appearance, it is possible for a Nosferatu ghoul to become physically degenerate. Usually, such flaws are not revealed until the third and final stage of the blood bond. The mark of evil is typically only a slight taint: A stoop, twisted teeth or blotchy skin are typical examples.

If a Nosferatu ghoul serves his master for too long, however, his degeneracy can transform him into a pitiful and abominable creature. Ghouls who repeatedly take on tasks that are morally reprehensible, deeds that even their masters would not attempt, may become subhuman, exhibiting leprous skin, a loss of speech or a loping, doglike gait. Such creatures are treasured by Bestials, not only for their sinister appearance but also because they typically learn to shun the world above. Once a ghoul can no longer pass himself off as human, he is willing to abandon the world of men and descend into the lowest levels of a Nosferatu kingdom.

Underground ghouls forever forsake the light of day. They serve with a loyalty unparalleled in any creature, willing to serve for an eternity, if necessary, performing the most reprehensible tasks in a Nosferatu warren. Their only "flaw," aside from their inhuman appearance, is the brutality they exhibit when they succumb to frenzy. Subhuman ghouls often develop a taste for human flesh that rivals their addiction to vitae and regularly indulge in secret orgies where they gleefully consume the flesh of the dead (or even worse, the living).

It is said that some ghouls have learned to rebel against their vampiric masters, forming their own subterranean colonies. Rumors proclaim that some have developed an immunity to the blood bond; they revile those of their kind who so readily serve vampiric society. There are legends (typically repeated by jaded neonates) that these ghouls have found other sources of vitae, either by capturing neonate vampires, allying with Solitaries or Leatherfaces or harboring revenants who have also forsaken vampiric society. No proof of these allegations have been found — merely underground chambers leading to the cemeteries of small towns, feeding pits lined with human bones and caerns of skulls bearing what distinctly appear to be vampiric fangs.

V:tM System: There is no proof that the subhuman variety of ghoul even exists... although... if it did... it would have Strength +2, Stamina +2, Intelligence 1 and Appearance 0. Subterranean ghouls have an additional weakness: They frenzy more frequently than weaker ghouls. For each week that passes after a ghoul's last frenzy, increase the difficulty of all of its Self-Control rolls by one. Subhumans will try to avoid this curse by regularly staging events that draw out their most savage urges, gathering in secretive chambers or graveyards with a tasty assortment of fresh corpses arrayed before them. *Bon appétit.*

MET Subterranean Ghouls: Create a basic human ghoul according to **Laws of the Night**. Such creatures may not take Social Traits related to Appearance, such as *Alluring* or *Gorgeous* — they are becoming too inhuman to look like or relate to normal humans. Should they frenzy, they gain a Negative Trait related to something subhuman, such as *Bestial* or *Callous*, in addition to any normal loss of Morality. When a subterranean ghoul encounters a mortal or vampire, make a Static

Self-Control Challenge (lose on ties). Should he lose or tie, he is immediately overcome with a tremendous hunger for her flesh and blood, and drags her into the warrens to feed on her. A subterranean ghoul venturing above ground in daylight takes no damage from sunlight, but may (at Storyteller discretion) be stunned for several turns and may suffer penalties in any challenges that require him to be in full light.

HORRID DIVERSIONS

Immortality is the greatest blessing a sire can bestow upon his childer... and the worst possible curse an elder can endure. Staying "forever young" may be appealing to some vampires, but for Nosferatu, the gift comes with an obvious drawback. When you spent eternity listening to the dim echoes of the vibrant world above, existence can be rather bleak. Fortunately, Nosferatu have no end of horrid diversions to distract them and occupy their time on this Earth (or beneath the earth, as the case may be).

INFORMATION NETWORKS

The Nosferatu have an unparalleled reputation as information brokers or, as some would say, spies. They have a habit of turning up dirty little secrets most vampires would never find. While Camarilla vampires have learned that the Sewer Rats habitually have access to information no one else can find, most are completely unaware of how they actually discover it.

Nosferatu "unity" accounts for a great deal of the clan's stranglehold on information. Most Nosferatu routinely trade secrets no Ventrue or Tremere would dare disclose. Even Camarilla and Sabbat Nosferatu trade knowledge about their respective sects, albeit for a *very* high price. This sense of cooperation between Sewer Rats and Creeps doesn't just arise out of goodwill, though: Both sects are threatened by tales of the Nictuku. According to legend, these Ancients are so stealthy that they could easily infiltrate a city and eliminate an entire warren. Cooperation is thus the clan's surest avenue to survival. No Nosferatu is ever obliged to trade away a secret he wants to hoard, but by exchanging what he has learned, he becomes richer with every transaction.

Of course, this freedom of information can be taken too far. Just because a vampire has Nosferatu vitae coursing through his veins does not give him instant access to all the dark secrets he can remember. Data always comes with a price. From the moment a Nosferatu enters another Sewer Rat's domain, he receives hints, requests or outright threats for information. The Fifth Tradition insists that any vampire respects the domain of another. If a Nosferatu wants to use the resources of others of his kind (which he invariably needs to do), he's naturally going to be asked to perform a few favors in return. Broods need such information to survive; they'll barter it carefully for maximum returns.

Spies are the most important aspect of a Nosferatu's web. Neonate Nosferatu who work with broods are enlisted for one of the most dangerous — and most educational — tasks a Sewer Rat can attempt: watching the other vampires of the city. Elder Nosferatu give these childer a relatively simple task: Watch and learn. The ones who get caught, of course, deserve to get punished, usually by the vampires who uncovered their insidious activities. An elder who is besieged by fledgling vampires (say, as new players in a live-action troupe) would be wise to send them out unseen to observe the world outside the sewers.

A Nosferatu should never discount the usefulness of animal spies. The Animalism Discipline allows Creeps and Sewer Rats to gather simple information from creatures many vampires overlook while they conduct clandestine business. Rats scurry in and out of some of the most inaccessible buildings in a city. Alley cats are quickly dismissed as harmless by soft-hearted humans and oblivious Kindred. Watchdogs will wait for hours outside a building in return for a scant bit of praise from their masters. Birds have no trouble soaring overhead to watch movements on the ground. Of course, the quality of such information is limited by the intelligence of the animals, but sometimes, just knowing who goes where at what times within a city is enough to give a Nosferatu an edge over other vampires.

Nosferatu also have numerous social amusements involving the transfer of rumors and secrets. Mastery of mnemonic games is one of their specialties. One of the most popular games is similar to a well-known children's game. The youngest vampire in the room begins by stating a secret that he knows; the next oldest may repeat the first secret, adding one of his own. Elders who look down on such childish entertainment leave the room, but neonates can spend hours swapping trash in this way. If a Nosferatu forgets part of the chain or adds a secret that can't compare to the ones before it, he's forced to leave the room as well. Of course, elders also cheat at this game, lurking nearby while the youngsters spill their guts.

To pass long nights in the sewers, Nosferatu also gather with others of their kind to exchange stories of the surface world. For Sewer Rats who never venture into the world above, such tales are often their only source of information. Nosferatu storytelling is legendary. It is ideal art for such hideous creatures, especially since it relies entirely on the voice. In tunnels obscured by complete darkness, the most dramatic storytellers can captivate a brood of neonates with nothing but carefully chosen words and inflections. Epic stories are passed from brood to brood, sometimes in exchange for passing through a domain. One caveat is essential here, however: Rarely, if ever, are the greatest Nosferatu stories told to anyone except another Nosferatu.

One might very well argue that because of the number of antisocial vampires in the clan, boredom is the final reason contributing to the success of Nosferatu information networks. Nosferatu who refuse to interact with others have more time to kill than typical Kindred and Cainites. For Nosferatu, social events are not a priority, rendezvous with mortals only endanger their survival, and clan politics are far too shallow a pursuit. Feeding is relatively easy, since most Nosferatu are not particular about where they get their blood, and companionship (other than the occasional coterie) is a rarity. When a solitary Nosferatu has a chance to host others of his kind, gossip can be a welcome relief from countless nights of skulking alone beneath the city. Bingeing and purging a host of nasty little secrets in one evening can sustain a sewer dweller for a long, long time.

SCANDALS

Honesty is crucial among Nosferatu, no matter how ugly the truth might be. When trading information, Sewer Rats should do more than just spread dirt around; when dealing with their own kind, they should disclose how trustworthy their sources are, evaluate how true a rumor might be and stake their reputation on the absolute infallibility of their news only when necessary. There is only one segment of Nosferatu society that does not adhere to these guidelines: the Scandals.

Nosferatu Scandals regularly deal in rumors that would make the average tabloid journalist blush. If you believe what a self-proclaimed Scandal is selling, you deserve what you get. Information traders of this sort specialize in salacious gossip, outrageous reports and outright innuendo. One of the best examples of the work of a Nosferatu Scandal was the epic story of the "Bat Child," an escaped Nosferatu fleeing from mortal authorities on fluttering, chiropteran wings. The tales the Scandals fabricated about this creature were so sensational that they were eventually repeated in a common supermarket tabloid over the course of several months. This one legend, more than any other, has made scandalous tabloid-style reporting eminently popular among a new generation of neonate Nosferatu. Although such stories are rarely believed, there is always a hunger for such "infotainment." Enquiring minds still want to know.

Will Work for Blood

Pasty, bloated, antisocial, greasy-haired misfits — do those words describe Nosferatu or the lowest lifeforms the Internet has to offer? Both groups are nailed with the same crude stereotypes. To become truly proficient in the world of computers, some humans retreat from all social contact, ignore simple matters of personal hygiene and reject mainstream standards of self-esteem as they're drawn further and further into another world. Is that an unfair description? Even if it is, the reputation of hackers is base enough to attract the attention of elder Nosferatu who know *nothing* of the information superhighway. In a desperate attempt to understand the modern world, broods are recruiting a whole new generation of hackers and computer freaks into the clan. Swap the Erg Cola and O'Tolley's take-out for the occasional chance to suck on human blood, and the lifestyle is not all that different.

Enough computer-savvy vampires have been inducted into the clan to erect an entirely new social phenomenon among the undead: SchreckNET, a virtual domain crawling with cyber-clueful Nosferatu. The Nosferatu have taken up the tools of the information age with a passion, especially ones that allows them to interact with each other completely undetected, without having to see (or smell) each other. Appearance means nothing in this domain. Neonate hackers don't go in for icons, avatars, scanned photographs or "virtual" representations — they learn the identity of other computer creeps solely by the words they employ and the thoughts they convey.

Just as their elders have social protocols, Nosferatu have developed their own codes of conduct for e-mail and chat rooms. On the rare occasions when another supernatural creature hacks its way inside, a breach of antisocial etiquette can force a whole chat room of Nosferatu to disappear and coalesce "somewhere else" on the Net. And of course, as one would expect, SchreckNET users choose their words very carefully, since any forum can be surrounded by hosts of lurkers.

Modern broods may see the value of keeping a Nosferatu hacker on hand, providing him with enough blood and tech to devote himself entirely to his craft. Through chat rooms, encrypted e-mail messages, bulletin boards, encoded web pages and the like, users passing through the SchreckNET hub continue to pass along information used by one of the most extensive nocturnal conspiracies in the world. The Internet never sleeps, and SchreckNET keeps its information gateways open all night.

Scavenger Hunts

Take practical training in espionage, throw in contempt for other supernatural creatures, and add a dose of bloody good fun. The result is a traditional Nosferatu pastime elders call the *aranta-shadur*. Neonates know it as a "scavenger hunt." It begins with the clan elders assembling all the neonates and ancillae in a warren for a Hosting. The elders then distribute a list of items that are closely tied to other vampires in the city. Usually the chosen objects satirically comment on the vampires who own them. Typical examples include a Toreador poseur's full-length mirror, a pretentious Tremere magus' favorite cloak or the brand-new and untouched leather jacket from an intellectual Brujah's closet.

Each participant also has a few special items tailored to his skill and generation. A neonate, for instance, wouldn't have much of a chance of stealing the prince's signet ring, but an ancilla probably could. If the elders wish to test especially promising Sewer Rats, they may ask more than one Nosferatu to acquire a particularly rare item. Exceptionally powerful competitors may even be expected to abduct mortals or even other vampires as part of their list. On rare occasions, the local Nosferatu may invite vampires from other clans to participate. Anyone who's better at gathering dirt than the Nosferatu certainly deserves their respect, so winning a Nosferatu scavenger hunt can garner an impressive amount of prestige.

There is one stipulation to this sport: All items must be acquired surreptitiously, without the knowledge of their owners. This is a test of stealth and cunning, not of intimidation or combat ability. As with the mundane version of this amusement, the competitor who steals the most items by the deadline (usually about a two hours before sunrise) wins. The last two hours are essential for the final step of the *aranta-shadur*, when the items are returned to the places they were found.

But Is It Art?

Contrary to what some Degenerates say, every vampiric society, every supernatural clan and every collective of night stalkers in a given city has its own version of "art." From the Brujah rebel's rants and raves to the Ventrue capitalist's quarterly report, every vampire has his own particular form of expression. Nosferatu have artistic endeavors as well, though admittedly, many of them are crafted for the sole purpose of offending other Kindred's delicate sensibilities.

Nosferatu art falls into two extremes: It either thrives on shock value, or it reveals a depth of humanity that's even more shocking. Unlike the egotistical displays of other clans, Nosferatu art is particularly bizarre because the artist doesn't necessarily expect his work to be seen. In fact, many of the greatest works of Nosferatu art have been hidden in chambers of absolute darkness, never to be viewed... until the right vampire walks into a place where he shouldn't be. Make of this moral what you will.

One of the most common media of Nosferatu art is sculpture, particularly since Nosferatu artists have no shortage of raw materials. With the Potence Discipline, smashing, bending and chiseling out massive works of art is surprisingly easy. Some of the most isolated tunnels of the sewers serve as an ideal "gallery." One popular approach is lining underground tunnels with mile after mile of spiraling tubes, electrical wires and sheet metal. Such works not only have aesthetic value but also serve as psychological warfare: An outsider wandering too deep within a city sewer may be terrified to discover how elaborate such works really are.

Sound is not only a popular medium, but a practical one. Nosferatu "sound rooms" are oddly shaped chambers designed to echo bizarre acoustical effects. Sometimes the emanations reverberate for miles down a corridor, scaring the hell out of anyone who doesn't realize where the sounds originate. More importantly, auditory art can also mislead and misdirect creatures who would invade a Nosferatu's domain. A common variant involves guttural "singing" — inhuman noise takes on an even eerier quality when it's echoing from five directions at once. Sabbat Nosferatu sometimes treat their victims to a private recital, providing a musical accompaniment as they stalk their fleeing prey though the underworld.

"Water chambers" combine sound and visuals to create viscous, dripping masterpieces. Cavernous, echoing chambers filled with dripping pipes leak foul fluids on taut drums of human skin, twisted vibrating metal or rows and rows of human skulls. Cracks are chiseled with a precision that establishes a steady rhythm. Condensation weeps bizarre melodies on the trash piles gathered beneath it. The result is entirely alien, meticulously grotesque and strangely compelling.

Fun with Fungus

If music is not to an elder's liking, he may prefer to study the art of agriculture. Granted, a Nosferatu's knowledge of plants is often limited to specimens that grow in darkness and fecal abundance. This includes a vast array of mycological wonders. The most extensive Nosferatu kingdoms include vast "fungal chambers," where Sewer Rats cultivate growths that defy scientific classification. Psychedelic mushrooms, semi-intelligent oozes, gelatinous blobs and spore-chucking carpets of bacteriological horror all thrive in the moist, steamy, yeasty interiors of Nosferatu gardens.

It is rumored that in the Kingdom of Manhattan, Sabbat Nosferatu kidnap human victims and toss them into their carefully cultivated subterranean forests of fungi. There, mortals are forced to ingest exotic and often lethal hallucinogens. As they "trip to death," drug-addled Nosferatu feed on them, enjoying a delightful alternative to the standard "suck-and-shuck." Camarilla vampires tell tales of Creeps indulging in fungal-enhanced orgies before they set out for their war parties. Camarilla Sewer Rats remain curiously silent about these rumors and skulk back to their own fungal kingdoms.

Interview with a Vampire

Cynicism and pessimism are essential to a Nosferatu's survival. Most vampires of this clan don't try to delude themselves about their clan or their place in the world. They don't explain away their atrocities with noble sentiments; because they have to accept themselves for what they really are, they must face reality no matter how ugly it gets. And because Nosferatu spend so much time removed from many Camarilla activities, whether by circumstance, social ostracism or preference, they also hold a rather objective view of the failings of other clans. We don't need to tell you any more. It's better to let some of the Sewer Rats tell you themselves... or maybe even one of their victims....

New Orleans, 1999

From my flat in the Vieux Carré, my guest looks out upon the city with his *old eyes*, speaking softly of the torment he has had to endure for centuries. He is beautiful, rather like a god, as I expect all vampires are. Six-foot tall and thoroughly Anglo-Saxon, he is beautiful enough to inspire love at first sight. Although I can scarcely believe my good fortune, I sit at the table before him with my tape recorder, faithfully recording my interview with the undead. As he tosses his golden hair over his shoulder, he poses in the neon light. "So," he says in his angelic voice, "you would like to learn about our Masquerade, would you?" As he carefully chooses his words, I cannot avoid gazing at his thick, sensuous lips.

"Indeed!" I shout. "I have been writing about your kind all my life. I've spent years searching for you. I've even left my telephone number in a hundred different phone booths in New Orleans, hoping you might answer. And now you are here!" I am so ecstatic that I can hardly breathe; instead, I babble with praise. "Did you have a chance to read the novel I sent you?"

As he continues musing, I find myself growing rather queasy. An odd smell is building in the room. "Yes, I read it. I'll even tell you what I think of it," he says, his voice dropping a full octave. The guttural sound that follows mutates into a raspy, grating sound. As his façade is dropped, I see the vampire for what he really is. His blond hair turns into greasy dreadlocks; his skin withers into a brittle, reptilian cast. He hunches in his chair, and suddenly, the faint aroma of perfume I found so delightful becomes the unspeakable tang of a bathroom urinal cake.

"What's the matter, kid? Who were you expecting? Brad Pitt?" The next sound on my tape recorder is the prolonged sound of retching as I vomit profusely....

THE CAMARILLA

"Is this thing still on? Good. Here's the story you want: The Masquerade hides six families of vampire in Camarilla society, the little conspiracy we've been maintaining for the last 500 years. Yeah, yeah, I've read your damn novels, and you don't know shit about vampires. I wouldn't use those books to wipe my ass. Killing humans onstage in Paris? Vampire rock stars? What the hell were you thinking?

"I don't usually deal with humans, mainly because I hate your kind so much. That's why we've got the Camarilla: We don't want to deal with humans at all, so we've got this epic society to keep us distracted from human concerns. Actually, the other vampires like to treat it like it's a big social event, but just you wait. When the shit hits the fan, the pretty vampires you write about are gonna be the first ones to hit the rotating blades.

"Of course, some Kindred claim that we actually manipulate every aspect of human society. Don't believe it. It's all bullshit. Me, I got nothing but contempt for your race, and I'd prefer to have nothing to do with it. That's why my kind are called Sewer Rats. We live in the midst of your society and thoroughly infiltrate it, but we stay hidden the entire time. Oh yeah, and like rats, we don't mind shitting where we live...."

THE SABBAT

"Just in case that's too pleasant for you, I know a group a vampires who hate the human race even more than I do. This other bunch, the Sabbat, know you for the vain and destructive little bastards you are. To you, vampires are some kind of poetic metaphor; to them, a human being is just another blood bag. Human life means nothing to them, so they'll get away with killing as many of you as they need to survive. You're lucky you didn't attract a few of them with your pathetic bathroom scrawls. Sabbat Nosferatu revel in being as freakish and unsightly as possible — even more than me! — and love to give anyone who deals with them the Creeps. Hence their nickname."

BRUJAH

"Both the Sabbat and the Camarilla have other kinds of vampires as well, and they're not all artsy-fartsy pretty boys. Like I was saying, there are seven major clans. First off, there's the Brujah, who'd just as soon kill you as look at you. You'd probably think of them as leather-clad Lost Boys, and they'd probably love to stomp you into the pavement because of it. They're violent and unpredictable, no matter how intellectual they make themselves out to be. Quite frankly, the hero of your vampire novel would get his head bashed in by one of these guys.

"You've always got to watch what you say around a Brujah. Most of them are a little too eager to get into a fight. Then again, they often forget how strong many Nosferatu are. If it comes down to a match between speed and strength, I'll bet on me every time. We do business with them, but that doesn't mean we like them. Selling information to rebellious Brujah is easy, since they're always looking for an edge against their enemies. A lot of them are gullible: Spread a few lies around one of the local Rants, and they'll charge off in seven directions at once, like all Gehenna's broken loose."

GANGREL

"Then there the Outlanders, the vampires who walked away from the Camarilla. They've always preferred the wilderness to the cities, and they have a tendency to wander where they will. Sometimes I wonder why we didn't think of leaving the Camarilla before they did. They generally treat us better than any other clan. I think it's because most of them have gone off into a frenzy a few times too many. A lot of them just want to be left alone — just like most Nosferatu do — so we tend to get along just fine."

MALKAVIANS

"What can I say about the Malkavians? Damn freaks. Can't stand 'em. They're dangerously unbalanced. I've seen 'em act the fool one moment and then slash up someone with a razor blade the next. The Malkavians are all crazy — I hate having to do business with someone with multiple personalities."

TOREADOR

"Then there are the Toreador. You want me to tell you what I think of the Toreador?" (Much to my alarm, the next sound on my tape recorder was a lengthy, gaseous emission of preternatural proportions emanating from the vampire's nether regions.) "They're so damn fascinated by beauty that they've forgotten how ugly their kind really is. Vampires pretending to be beautiful humans? Fawning over the prettiest portions of the mortal world? It's like Jackson Pollock said...." (My guest then proceeded to vomit blood on a nearby bedsheet, an artistic display my tape recorder simply could not record or reproduce.)

TREMERE

"The Tremere are known as the Warlocks, since they study the dark arts. They're creepy and they're kooky... mysterious and spooky.... and the most doomed vampires on Earth. They're all bound together through a blood curse, spending all eternity struggling against each other for power and authority within their clan. While their sorcery makes 'em strong, it's not worth the price of being trapped in this clan forever. They talk a lot about loyalty, but the truth is, anyone one of them would screw over any other for a slight boost up their 'pyramid of power,' or whatever the hell they call it. As far as business goes, they're always hungry for occult secrets or anything that helps them screw over their own kind."

VENTRUE

"The Ventrue are fools. Wealthy, influential, powerful fools. Most of them seem to think they're the most qualified to lord over the Camarilla, and I say let 'em have it. If they want to stand at the vanguard of the Cam, then that means they'll be the first ones to get killed off when the next Sabbat crusade comes to town."

CAITIFF

"Finally, there are the Caitiff, or clanless — the lost darklings rejected by their creators. The Caitiff are the only vampires in the world who get screwed over more than we do. Then again, it's good to know we aren't on the bottom of the dog pile, right? We need someone to screw over, too, so if that's the way it's gotta be, too damn bad."

ASSAMITES

"Okay, so there are other clans, too, out in the dark places of the world. Take the Assamites, for instance. You know, a lotta Kindred talk about these guys like they're assassins and not much else. I've dealt with some, though, that are more successful as scholars, as students of the occult, that kind of thing. They've also got grudges with the Ventrue that go back a long way, so that makes them worth dealing with."

RAVNOS

"I don't really give a damn about the Deceivers one way or the other. We've got nothing worth stealing, and they don't usually come begging us for information. If they screw over Toreador and Ventrue, that's all right with me."

GIOVANNI

"Y'know, I'm used to being surrounded by vampires I can't see. I have no idea how I'm supposed to protect myself against the dead. I've only got rumors about how the Giovanni barter with ghosts to spy on us all. Of course, if they aren't trading that information away, it's kind of a waste."

SETITES

"These guys are an enigma. They're supposed to be, like, a pack of little blood cultists, trying to carry out some spooky master plan for the Death God Set, but then again, aren't all the Camarilla Kindred supposed to be pawns of their Ancients, too? They've got a talent for corrupting and exploiting people, but I'm not so sure they're any better at it than other vampires."

INTRUDERS

Learning about the other supernatural creatures in the world takes a little more work than studying other

Kindred and Cainites, but the Nosferatu have pieced together enough hidden secrets to get by. One aspect of Nosferatu society, the Loremasters, spends an eternity trying to understand other occult creatures and don't share their information too readily. The average Nosferatu pusbag has a less informed but far more colorful view of them. The opinions that follow were transcribed from an audio tape fished from the sewers of New Orleans....

LUPINES

"The Lupines are night-prowling monsters through and through. I saw a Nosferatu crush the skull of one of these puppies' with a single blow, but I'm guessing it was a lucky shot. I'd saying hiding from them would be the safest choice.

"I have seen, however, that there are a few Lupines that are just about as down and out as we are. When a wolf pack takes down its prey, the leaders get first shot at the prime bits of meat, but there's always got to be some straggler that winds up chewing on the bones. I've met a few of these homeless werewolves — of course, I don't know whether to trust these guys or just throw a steak over my shoulder and run."

MAGES

"In some ways, these guys are worse than Tremere. Fortunately, I think they're rather weak. I mean, they're mortal after all, right? Even knives and guns are lethal to a sorcerer. I also hear their version of magic's got a funny way of backfiring on them. Not so tough — I'm surprised these Renaissance rejects didn't die out a long time ago."

GHOSTS

"Yeah, sure I believe in ghosts. Buncha spooky guys hiding from the real world, but unlike the Nosferatu, they can't touch it. As far as I can tell, they can't do much of anything except watch what's going on and lament. What? Do you think one's watching us right now? Tell him to watch me do this...."

FAERIES

"Oooh! Look at the cute little faeries! Dancing around, singing poetry and shit! If you ripped its wings off, it'd probably bleed to death. Big deal."

HUNTERS

"Hunters? Human? Don't believe it. I don't know where these freaks learned to kill so efficiently, but with some of the powers they use, you know they ain't human no more. Some Loremaster told me once that their possessed by angels or something, but I think he's full of it. I've got no respect for a vampire who's sloppy enough to kill the kine he feeds from. I've got even less respect for a human who thinks its his moral duty to kill off as many vampires as he can. Hunters are just another kind of monster, as far as I'm concerned."

ADVERSARIES

The underworld is vast, and while the Nosferatu may lay claim to all of it, other monsters are eager to contest for control. Fleeing in the sewers may allow a Sewer Rat to escape the hazards of the surface world, but in the Gothic-Punk world, there are other creatures eager to remain unseen. The greatest among them are the legendary Nictuku, Ancients that predate all other concerns of Clan Nosferatu.

THE NICTUKU

By now, you've heard the legend: Nosferatu, the Antediluvian cursed by Caine, despised himself and what he had done so much that he began killing his own childer. Allegedly, the other Antediluvians must wait for Gehenna before they awaken and devour their descendants, but Nosferatu has already been slaying his own kind for millennia. Nosferatu's eldest childer, the Nictuku, are rumored to stalk the underworld, winnowing the weakest vampires of the clan until the carnage of the End Times begins.

The Nosferatu pride themselves on gathering some of the darkest secrets of vampiric society, but rumors and legends of the Nictuku abound. So far, most Loremasters agree that the Nictuku are not a bloodline, but actually include most of the fourth-generation Nosferatu — most, but not all. If this is true, it raises a host of questions. What precisely has happened to Nosferatu's other childer? Did they die out? Or have they been slumbering for millennia, waiting for the chance to rise up and devour their scattered relations? Do they even exist? Is the lie a tool to unite Camarilla Nosferatu against a common enemy?

Rumor has it that the Nictuku have far more of the original Antediluvian's vitae coursing through their veins. Some vampiric scholars even insist that they are all blood bound to the sleeping Ancient, acting as his eyes and ears (and tendrils and tentacles) throughout the world. There is no evidence of the Nictuku actually existing, though — in fact, the only hints of their existence are the scattered ashes of their alleged victims.

Regardless, Nosferatu who choose to remain isolated from the rest of the clan continue to disappear mysteriously. This is the primary reason so many Nosferatu spend eternity hiding. Elders insist that only constant vigilance can put an end to these disappearances. A few are obsessed with the legend, rigorously investigating any rumor of a Nictuku presence. In response, neonates often scoff that the story is nothing more than a tactic used by elder Nosferatu to foster clan unity. They have sighted enough shambling horrors in the underworld beneath cities without having to blame killings on legendary creatures. As the debate mounts, so does the body count.

OTHER CRITTERS

Still feel safe underground? What's the skittering noise around the next bend of the tunnel? No wonder so many of the Nosferatu have to work together — just keeping their own underground kingdoms safe takes eternal vigilance and epic cooperation.

Wetbrains: Human beings, burned out on drugs or booze, crawl into the most unlikely places. According to Loremasters, sometimes "evil spirits" consume their souls and crawl inside of them. Whether that's true, these foul and filthy rejects are not completely human — they're desperate for food and (if the legends are right) for human souls, too. Crawling down into sewers, storm drains, alleyways and ditches, they twitch and shiver until hunger consumes them again.

Diseases and infections corrupt these shambling, half-human "zombies"; some are transmitted repeatedly when they rut with each other out of boredom and desperation. When the right piece of meat comes along, they'll drag it down into the depths with them for food or sex (or possibly both at the same time). Urban tribes of wetbrains congregate for communal survival. Some barely pass themselves off as homeless, recruiting other victims in the process. Occasionally, their shagging and porking will produce wetbrain offspring; if it isn't eaten, the child may survive without its parents' addiction. If it grows up, it'll no doubt gather a host of similar creatures.

Sewer Gators: Urban legend? So are vampires. Some of these mutations were bought by happy, little children on vacation in the Everglades... and flushed by angry, bitter parents back home. Feasting on sewage, hiding in garbage and occasionally snacking on pets and vagrants, they grow to a monstrous size. Some are albino, while others sport protective coloration (making Stealth rolls much easier). A few are blind, while others peer into the darkness with blazing red eyes. And, of course, a special few are raised as pets by Nosferatu... or do the oldest ones raise Nosferatu as pets? Sewer Rat storytellers suspect both legends are true. Then again, to some, all urban legends are true. For alligator stats, turn to the back of **Vampire: the Masquerade**.

Rats!: Colonies of scurrying rodents scamper throughout the city, feasting off garbage, spreading disease and avoiding obviously supernatural creatures who want to use them as disposable allies. Like all feral animals, they have a fierce survival instinct, and even when in the throes of Animalism, they have little reason to perform suicidal tasks for mysterious strangers. Still, they are experts on infiltrating human territories (often taking them as their own) and occasionally roam the sewers in packs. An average pack of *Rattus norvegicus*, for instance,

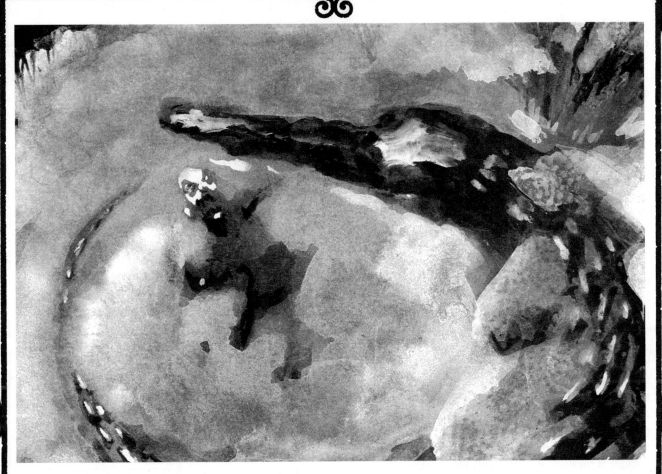

may consist of up to 60 rodents... if you see one coming your way, perhaps you should take another sewer tunnel. Rat stats are also in **Vampire: the Masquerade**.

A Festering Heap of Game Mechanics

Rules are meant to be broken or at least modified when they're inadequate. For Storytellers who want more game mechanics, here's a whole heap of them, scrounged from the world of the Nosferatu. Below are some more guidelines, suggestions and mechanics for Nosferatu characters, chronicles and adventures.

New Background: Information Network

You've got informants everywhere. You don't even need to go to them anymore — they come to you, and they bring all sorts of dirty little secrets to trade. The secrets you gather may be completely irrelevant to the problems you have right now, in which case you can always trade them away for something you can use. Any factoid or datum you harvest may seem irrelevant now but may be massively useful later; it may give you a vital lead that places you one step ahead of everyone else. (Note: At the Storyteller's

option, these same game mechanics may also be applied to the Contacts Background.)

V:tM System: At the beginning of each chapter of a story, roll a number of dice equal to the number of dots you have in this Background against difficulty 8. If you succeed, the Storyteller will give you a random rumor you've acquired from one of your informants. One success is a hint; three includes some commentary on the reliability of the rumor; five successes shouldn't shut down the evening's story, but it should reveal a secret valuable enough to elicit a favor from another supernatural creature in the city.

MET System: If your Storyteller allows it, you may purchase the *Information Network* during the freebie point phase of character creation. At the beginning of each session, make a Simple Test with the Storyteller. If you win, he gives you a bit of information that has been floating around the network (which may or may not be related to the current story). Alternately, your Storyteller may allow you to use it once per session as an "ear to the ground" to see if you can dig up something about your current interest (of course, what comes back need not have anything to do with the subject at hand, or even be truthful — *caveat emptor*). Your Storyteller may require you to detail something about who or what makes up your network. This Background functions separately from the *Contacts* Background, in that it utilizes *only* the local rumor mills, water cooler gossips and the like, while *Contacts* are more specific.

Nosferatu and the Lore Ability

Nosferatu trade in all sorts of secrets, including the deepest mysteries of the occult sciences. In game terms, the Secondary Ability Lore (or one of its many incarnations) represents the field of knowledge peculiar to a Loremaster. Each area of the outré or supernatural has its own particular variant, whether that's Sewer Lore, Camarilla Lore, Sabbat Lore or something even more exotic. This skill isn't used purely to remember esoteric knowledge; it can also help an occultist discern, largely from context, attitude, references and presentation, whether another Loremaster is telling the truth or wildly fabricating and speculating to misdirect someone he doesn't respect. This can also be attempted with the Occult Knowledge, but only with at least five levels and the appropriate specialization. Keep in mind that the Nosferatu have their own culture built around such transactions; Tremere, mortal mages, Arcanum hunters and academic crackpots each have their own cultural standards for exchanging occult knowledge.

Any subject worthy of the esoteric lore contains a hierarchy of secrets, from the outer mysteries taught to an initiate to the inner secrets hoarded by esoteric masters. In both the tabletop and live-action version of this game, the Lore Ability has at least five dots (or five levels) of specialization. A Nosferatu with a higher Lore Ability than another seeker of knowledge has secrets so obscure that he may not want to trade them with lesser initiates. For example, a live-action character with Cainite Lore x 5 may not want to share an apocryphal reference from *The Book of Nod* with someone who has Cainite Lore x 4. While such knowledge is commonly thought to be the stock and trade of the Tremere, remember that the Nosferatu are willing to deal in *any* type of secret. Regardless of clan, experts don't dispense with their trade secrets easily.

As such, the Lore Ability may also be used to evaluate how learned another Loremaster is. In live action, someone with this skill may attempt a Mental Challenge while questioning another occultist in matters of the supernatural; the winner of this test learns exactly how many Lore Traits his opponent has. In tabletop, each Loremaster rolls Lore; the difficulty for the roll is (10 - the level of Lore the vampire has).

Fooling someone into thinking you're more knowledgeable than you actually are may mean you can learn some secrets outsiders were not meant to know: Someone with four levels of Sabbat Lore may learn of a fragment of knowledge hoarded by scholars with five levels. The most esoteric secrets of Clan Nosferatu, like the masters of knowledge themselves, are hidden behind vast and labyrinthine corridors of misdirection and deceit. Enter their lair at your own risk.

Merits and Flaws

Storytellers tend to either love or hate Merits and Flaws. As always, they should feel free to limit, modify, accept or ban them as they see fit. For players of White Wolf's **Mind's Eye Theater**, many of the descriptions are followed by rules for adapting these optional traits for live action. As always, using one of these edges or handicaps requires the permission of a Storyteller or Narrator.

Lizard Limbs (1-pt. Merit)

With a little bit of effort, you can shed parts of your body. When one of your appendages is restrained or grappled, spend one blood point and roll Willpower (difficulty 8). If you succeed, you can tear off that body part and wriggle away. Vampires can eventually regrow their limbs if they spend enough blood; however, if you're missing an arm or leg, you should have a -3 dice pool penalty to represent your injury. And remember to be careful: If you shed both your legs, you'll have a bitch of a time crawling away.

MET: By burning a Blood Trait and a Willpower Trait, you can shed one of your limbs. You can do this for as much blood and Willpower you're willing to sacrifice. Gain the Negative Trait: *Lame* while you're without the limb (you receive no extra Traits for it). Roleplay the deformity until it grows back.

Long Fingers (1-pt. Merit)

Your fingers are unnaturally long and spidery. You gain an extra die on any roll involving coordination or grappling.

MET: Gain the Physical Trait *Dexterous*, and a one-Trait bonus in all challenges involving manual dexterity.

Oversized Fangs (1-pt. Merit)

You have enormous fangs, snaggly tusks resembling those of an elephant or walrus. They cannot be retracted, but they do an additional die of damage and add one die to your Intimidation dice pool.

MET: Gain two bonus Traits useful in any biting attack. Your bite does an extra level of damage.

PISCINE (1-PT. MERIT)

You are abnormally comfortable underwater and vastly prefer swimming to walking. You get a -1 difficulty on any Physical dice pool related to underwater movement.

MET: Gain a bonus Trait during any challenge related to swimming or movement through water; this Trait is available to you only when you are at least chest-deep in water.

SLIMY (1-PT. MERIT)

Like a worm or mollusk, you have skin that secretes an oozing slime. Your difficulty to soak fire damage is reduced by one, and opponents who try to grapple you must score two more successes than normal.

MET: Gain an extra Health Level for resisting fire damage, plus two bonus Traits when someone is trying to grapple you.

GAPING MAW (2-PT. MERIT)

You've got a nasty gash where your mouth should be. It can smile, it can frown, and most importantly, it can grin two or three inches wider than any human mouth can. An ordinary vampire can suck up to three blood points in a turn. You can drain up to four points a turn, provided you can latch your tooth-filled orifice around enough skin.

MET: You can drain a victim for four Blood Traits each turn instead of three.

PROJECTILE VOMITING (2-PT. MERIT)

This talent is like the Eat Food Merit, but twice as versatile. Food comes in; food goes out very, very fast. A vampire with this ability can ingest, and possibly even taste, food and drink. He cannot gain any nutritional benefit from this ordinarily digestible matter, but he can store it for later use. When this need arises, the Nosferatu can not only disgorge his stored supply of food, but also aim it with a degree of precision.

For the record, projectile vomiting in the Storyteller system usually requires a Stamina + Athletics roll; the difficulty is 8, and a victim can attempt to dodge this bolus of ejected victuals. Although this attack does not cause damage (save to one's pride), the type of food ejected may temporarily obscure a victim's vision, cause him to slip or merely force him to weep with shame at a Camarilla Toreador's grand ball. Pity the poor vomit-drenched Toreador....

MET: Vomit doesn't work quite the same way other projectile weapons. If you're attempting to hit someone or something with this nasty missile, you must succeed in a Physical Challenge. Your victim may resist in the usual manner (modifiers for dodging and cover apply).

SLEEP UNSEEN (2-PT. MERIT)

You can use the Obfuscate Discipline to hide while you sleep during the day. Such prolonged use of this ability requires an extra blood point (or Blood Trait) to keep your body hidden for a full day. Of course, you must at least be hidden from sunlight, and vampires using the Auspex Discipline can still detect you, but mortals will ignore your very presence. This is a useful Merit for Nosferatu emissaries and travelers; many would perish without it.

MET: Spend an extra Blood Trait (in addition to any required by *Obfuscate*) before laying down to sleep. You must have Storyteller permission to take this Merit.

TOUGH HIDE (2-PT. MERIT)

Thick, leathery skin envelops you. Add an extra die when soaking damage (for anything except fire or sunlight).

MET: You have an additional Bruised Health Level.

FALSE REFLECTION (3-PT. MERIT)

When using Mask of a Thousand Faces, a Nosferatu with this Merit can create a false impression of his disguise on recording media. He can have his picture taken, show up on videotape and even record an imitation of the subject's voice. Nosferatu without this Merit cannot disguise themselves to machines using the Obfuscate Discipline.

MET: Spend a Mental Trait for each use of this (beyond any expenditure for *Mask of 1000 Faces* — so that's one Trait for your voice, one for your reflection, etc.). You should describe what the recording device picks up.

FOUL BLOOD (3-PT. MERIT)

The vitae flowing through your veins tastes truly awful. Anyone who bites or feeds from you must make a Willpower roll (difficulty 6) or spend the next turn choking, retching and gagging. Any idiot who actually tries to diablerize you must make three Willpower rolls (difficulty 9) to succeed.

MET: After biting or feeding from you, the victim must make a Simple Test to avoid becoming nauseated for a full scene; no spending Willpower to avoid the test (it tastes *that* bad). If the victim becomes nauseated, he suffers a one-Trait penalty on all Physical Challenges. This makes blood bonds torturous, the Embrace becomes even more difficult, and ghouling is near impossible.

REPTILE BUDDY (3-PT. MERIT)

Yes, those legends about albino alligators in the sewers really are true. You've been nursing a few of them with your vitae in the local spawning pool for years.

Your careful breeding and vigilant training has produced a reptilian slave of exceptional intelligence. It has a mind as sharp as that as a five-year-old child and teeth as keen as butcher knives. The beast understands your native language perfectly and can even follow complex directions. Faster and deadlier than any human ghoul, it is a highly efficient killing machine fully capable of patrolling your domain with ruthless efficiency. Reptile buddies also love to play "fetch" with human limbs (whether attached or severed).

Ghouled Reptile Buddy

Physical: Strength 6, Dexterity 2, Stamina 6
Social: Charisma 0, Manipulation 0, Appearance 0
Mental: Perception 3, Intelligence 1, Wits 3
Disciplines: Fortitude 2, Potence 2
Blood Pool: 5
Willpower: 5
Attacks: Bite (7 dice), Tail Slap (6 dice)
MET Stats
Physical Traits (7)
Social Traits (0)
Mental Traits (2)
Fortitude (Endurance, Mettle), Potence (Prowess, Might)
 Blood Pool 12
Willpower 3

PATAGIA (4-PT. MERIT)

Leathery wings fold up into your horrid little body. Picture the gliding wings of a pterodactyl or a flying squirrel. Now visualize them hanging off the twisted skeleton of batlike wings. With the aid of an updraft or a strong wind, you can glide for short distances — rather useful for Nosferatu who skulk along rooftops, don't you think? Storytellers should know that a vampire with this Merit can glide at his normal walking speed.

MET: You can't actually fly or hover with this Merit, only glide like a flying squirrel on flaps of leathery skin that stretch from under your arms and down your sides. You may not carry passengers and only personal items may travel with you (Storyteller discretion). Furthermore, you need wind to carry you, and if there's none, you just drop like a stone (so don't even think about using this indoors). When gliding, hold your arms out at your sides and wear a tag indicating your unusual appearance. You may glide at a normal walking speed. Consult the Storyteller before taking this Merit.

RUGGED BAD LOOKS (5-PT. MERIT)

Your face is hideous, but it could almost pass for that of a really ugly human. If you were to cover every other part of your body, you could shamble into mortal society looking only slightly suspicious. While you might have a hunchback, reptilian scales over parts of your flesh or a foul stench that never dissipates, you can actually walk among mortals — with extensive precautions — without automatically breaking the Masquerade. Other vampires give you no end of grief for not looking like a "real" Nosferatu. By the way, this is as "attractive" as a Nosferatu ever gets; no Merit will ever increase a Nosferatu's Appearance above zero.

BLUNT FANGS (1-PT. FLAW)

Your teeth are huge and square, not sharp like those of other vampires. To do damage with a bite attack, you must score an additional success (thus, this extra success subtracts from the amount of damage you do). Once you have sunk you teeth into your prey, you inflict a level of damage for every two blood points you take. Once your fangs are locked in a victim's flesh, you've got to chew and chew and chew....

MET: You need to make an extra Physical Challenge (in addition to any required to grapple your victim) in order to get your teeth in your victim. Your dulled bite does a level of damage to your victim for each Blood Trait you acquire.

INFAMOUS AUTARKIS (1-PT. FLAW)

The Camarilla won't accept you as one of its own under any circumstance. The Sabbat wouldn't think of submitting you to Creation Rites — it's just not worth it. Something in your past, your reputation or your sire's background is so abhorrent that both sects reject you utterly. You aren't just autarkis; your infamy spreads throughout both sects of vampiric society. Although you might find a coterie that's willing to work with you, they would not dare take you to any gathering of Camarilla or Sabbat vampires for fear of damaging their own reputations. The Storyteller may allow you to buy off this Flaw but only after you've completed a story in which you've resolved and overcome this social stigma.

MET: You may never gain Camarilla or Sabbat Status. This marks you as automatic prey for the Scourge in a Camarilla city, and for any likely hunters in a Sabbat city.

STENCH (1-PT. FLAW)

Even other Nosferatu recoil at your horrific odor. Subtract two dice from any Stealth roll when evading any creature that can smell (unless you are upwind).

MET: Lose all ties related to stealth automatically with this Flaw; it's pretty hard to sneak up on someone when he can smell you coming. You need not actually neglect personal hygiene to roleplay this Flaw. Wear a tag indicating your deformity

OPTIONAL NOSFERATU TRAITS

There's only so many times you can describe yourself as *Bestial*. Just how ugly is *Repugnant* anyway? Sometimes those words just don't quite seem to do justice to describe a spine curved like a bow, a wattled neck, a fanged maw or suppurating lesions. Would a back twisted with scoliosis and a face blighted by smallpox scars be less hideous if simply described as *Nasty*? With the Storyteller's permission, you may take these Traits to describe your more "outstanding" features. What follows are just a few — grab a thesaurus and get creative. However, if you're going to use these, remember to incorporate them into your roleplaying. These adjectives are no different as descriptors than, say, *Brawny* or *Impatient* might be.

Optional Nosferatu Traits: *Blighted, Blubbery, Charred, Dreadful, Engorged, Flaccid, Mangy, Nauseating, Oozing, Petrified, Putrefied, Pustulent, Reptilian, Repulsive, Rubbery, Scabrous, Scarred, Skanky, Withered.*

ANOSMIA (2-PT. FLAW)

You have no sense of smell or taste. The vilest odors and flavors imaginable cannot affect you; in fact, you do not even recognize their presence. You cannot attempt a Perception roll that involves either of these senses. However, any supernatural attack involving horrific odors and tastes does not affect you. Granted, Nosferatu who have surrounded themselves with unseemly funk long enough become immune to just about any foul odor, but you simply do not recognize smells at all.

MET: From the reek of spoiled milk to the delicate perfume of a magnolia in bloom, from the tang of blood on your tongue to the memory of your last martini, the world of scent and taste is lost to you. You may not take this Flaw and the Merits: *Acute Sense: Smell* or *Acute Sense: Taste*. You automatically lose any challenges relating to smell or taste; *Heightened Senses* for taste or smell has no affect on this.

PARASITIC INFESTATION (2-PT. FLAW)

Other creatures live on or inside you. Exotic hemovores — chiggers, gnats, ticks, lice, mosquitoes, leeches and unnamable bloodsucking fungal spores — consider the creases, folds and scabrous layers of your skin delightful. Your flesh continuously twitches and writhes, and living things burrow inside you, possibly even nesting in the cavities of your body. Despite all your ingenious methods of discouraging them, this loathsome hosting will not disperse. You cannot command these vermin in any fashion; in fact, the worst of them are very defiant because they have been strengthened and corrupted by your foul vitae.

Each day, when you rise, roll one die. Divide the result by three, rounding up. The result is the number of blood points you lose to the blood-intoxicated parasites within and upon you. In addition, the constant itching puts on you edge; increase the difficulty of all Self-Control rolls by one.

MET: When you go into play at the beginning of the evening, make the usual vitae test. Once you learn your level of vitae, make four Simple Tests — each loss or tie indicates a Blood Trait lost to your parasites. You suffer a one-Trait penalty during *Self-Control* tests. Roleplay the constant itching the parasites give you; also wear a tag to indicate to onlookers that your skin is quite literally crawling.

ENEMY BROOD (3-PT. FLAW)

A brood of your fellow Nosferatu have an unceasing vendetta against you. You can run from them, but you can't hide. If you stay in the same city, they will pool whatever resources they have to make your existence a living hell. Traveling through the local sewers is a nightmare. If you flee, they will use their influence and contacts to call in favors in the next city you show your ugly mug. The Storyteller may allow you to buy off this Flaw, but only after you've completed a story in which you've resolved and overcome this social stigma.

MET: This is a specialized variation of the Flaw: *Hunted*, found in **Laws of the Night**. Consult your Storyteller before you take it, and work with her to determine why you're hunted.

NECROPHILE (3-PT. FLAW)

No, you don't have sex with the dead, but you certainly enjoy their company. You are obsessed with dead bodies and "invite" them over to your domain. Your haven is distastefully decorated with severed and mutilated body parts of all kinds. You talk to your dead friends, dance with them, make art out of them and entertain frequently. Some vampires of particularly refined temperament may need to overcome a Courage roll (difficulty 4) to enter a room where you've left your guests and their accouterments. Toreador go apeshit; Toreador *antitribu* applaud. For some reason, this Flaw is very popular among Leatherfaces.

WITHERED LEG (3-PT. FLAW)

For whatever reason, one of your legs does not work as well as the other. You subtract three dice when attempting any action that involves movement, and you move at half normal speed.

MET: Gain the Negative Trait: *Lame x3* (but no benefits from it), and you fail any challenges that would require two good legs (such as running or dancing). Roleplay any difficulties in walking.

PUTRESCENT (4-PT. FLAW)

After you received the Embrace, your body continued to decay. The mystic processes that inhibit a vampire's natural putrefaction has little effect on you. As a result, you constantly rot. Subtract one die when your character soaks damage. If you are jarred or hit violently, roll Stamina (difficulty 6). If you fail, one of your facial features or limbs falls off. If you botch, you also take a level of aggravated damage; once this wound is healed, the missing body parts will regrow.

MET: Whenever you take damage, make a Static Test to see if the damage becomes aggravated due to your accelerated decay. You stink something awful, too — wear a tag whenever your true form is visible, proclaiming that you look and smell like a rotting corpse out of B-grade horror movie.

TRAITOR (4-PT. FLAW)

Oh, you're a bastard, all right, and if the other Nosferatu find out about this, they'll kill you on sight. You've been leaving information (through a designated drop point) about your alleged allies. This might involve regular e-mails, messages hidden at the same spot or a package you drop off for a courier. You must betray secrets about your allies, usually the members of your own coterie, every game session. At the end of the session, you must tell the Storyteller what you've done; if you haven't been enough of a bastard, one of *your* secrets winds up on the local information network.

CONTAGIOUS (5-PT. FLAW)

Dead bodies contain all sorts of infectious bacteria, fungi and spores. There's a reason coroners wear gloves when handling corpses. Thanks to a rather virulent version of Nosferatu's curse, a few doomed varieties of Nosferatu retain these infections after their Embrace. Contagious Nosferatu can never interact with mortals without the possibility of spreading sickness and disease. A mortal who touches a Contagious Nosferatu must make a Stamina roll (difficulty 9) or fall prey to illness for the next week. At the end of each week, the victim must make another roll; once he succeeds, he recovers from the illness.

While this may seem like a rather crippling Flaw, it does force players to think of new ways of interacting with the human world (many of which are detailed in this chapter). To maintain a sense of game balance, most other supernatural creatures have ways of dealing with

the Contagious Sewer Rat's disease: Werewolves regenerate very quickly, mages can mystically remove the infection from themselves or other mages, wraiths just don't give a damn because they're incorporeal, and so on.

INCOHERENT (5-PT. FLAW)

You are incapable of human speech. Maybe your jaw has collapsed or you've been abandoned in the sewers for too long. Pointing, grunting, wheezing and wildly gesturing are all within your repertoire, but actually forming words is not. While a player portraying this character can describe what he is doing, the character can never utter a word. The only exception to this is communicating with animals; you can express yourself to beasts with nonverbal language.

MET: Maybe your tongue fell out during your Embrace, or your vocal cords are atrophied from disuse. For whatever reason, you just can't speak clearly. You may use sign language or write out what you want to say, or you could just go for grunting and wild gestures. You may talk to your Storyteller or Narrator for rules purposes, but when in game, you must roleplay the Flaw.

CLAN DISCIPLINES

Elder Nosferatu who have studied the powers of the Blood for centuries devise many ingenious uses for their Disciplines. Neonates, on the other hand, often find themselves overwhelmed, unsure of what to do with this heady amount of power. For sires and childer alike, allow us to suggest a few unusual applications of your clan's primary disciplines, methods you might not have previously considered.

ANIMALISM

Animalism, the first "clan Discipline" of the Nosferatu, is easily one of the most underappreciated supernatural abilities. Neonates usually see a few obvious uses for this power and tend to be terribly amused the first few times they are able to converse with alley cats, sewer rats and roaming packs of feral dogs. They may even enjoy the first time they "summon up" a few of these urban creatures to attack others on their behalf. Elders are quick to point out, however, that there are other uses for this Discipline beyond the vampiric version of "Monster Summoning."

Scouts: Masters of the Obfuscate Discipline believe they are the most effective scouts and spies of vampiric society; they are sadly mistaken. While particularly perceptive Kindred may notice the Unseen Presence of Nosferatu, they often ignore the scouts that masters of Animalism recruit. With Feral Whispers, any alley cat or street rat can be instructed to take a quick look around a

corner, sneak inside a building or even shadow a suspicious character. Some Nosferatu have been known to carry around a pet specifically trained for this purpose; training one requires Animal Ken, of course.

Guard Dogs: Because Nosferatu are paranoid about being seen, it helps for them to have a few extra allies watching out for them. Training a watch dog or guard dog is much simpler with the Animalism Discipline than the Animal Ken Ability. Even a lowly cat or rat can be instructed to act as a lookout for a skulking Nosferatu.

Diversions: Ordinary urban animals are often ideal for planned diversions. Some neonates think that the Beckoning power is good only for staging an attack; however, as any good Sewer Rat knows, sneaking is often better than fighting. If you are being shadowed by your enemies in a public park, for instance, encouraging a flock of pigeons to flutter about your pursuers as a diversion is much easier than trying to summon up a flock of birds to peck them to death. Beckoning isn't intended to be used just on large groups of animals; a lone mortal walking his dog at night can create a host of opportunities a swarm of sewer rats does not.

Mental Manipulation: While not as effective as the Dominate Discipline, the Animalism power of Quell the Beast is an often overlooked way to manipulate mortals. By using this power effectively, a Nosferatu can convince a human witness that the presence of a skulking, sewer-dwelling monster is really not such a horrible threat after all. With a touch and a glance, a master of this ability can distract a witness long enough to bind and gag him, knock him senseless with Potence or give the other members of a coterie enough time to deal with him. Quell the Beast also makes for an excellent feeding technique.

Bestial Revelry: Some particularly bestial Nosferatu vastly prefer the Animalism power of Subsume the Spirit to Mask of a Thousand Faces. And why not? While an Obfuscated Nosferatu may be able to disguise himself as an innocuous human, a master of Animalism may freely roam the surface world as a rabid dog, feral cat or a more exotic sewer-dwelling creature. Auspex does not detect this possession.

Animal Spies: While a vampire with Heightened Senses may note a Nosferatu's Unseen Presence, he may have no qualms about speaking freely in front of the alley cat that just skulked in through the window of his haven. This oblivious attitude has made the information networks of many Nosferatu broods frighteningly effective. Even the most paranoid princes can't stop talking every time a rat scurries across the floor or a stray dog camps out on his haven's doorstep.

SONG IN THE DARK
Animalism Level Six

Before the clan could hide in labyrinths buried beneath the cities of men, Ancients relied upon vast caves and caverns for their survival. The most powerful Methuselahs didn't limit themselves to the few that existed — they created new ones. Loremasters tell tales of vast creatures underground, forgotten things from the early days of the world, monsters that Nosferatu himself could not destroy. Giants in the earth, these atavisms sluggishly tunnel and crawl countless miles beneath the surface world. Although cynical and scientific Nosferatu (autarkis or otherwise) deny the existence of such creatures, human scientists cannot fully predict the occurrence of earthquakes and similar subterranean events.

Some Nosferatu occultists claim that only Nosferatu Methuselahs are potent enough to draw upon this power. A few insist that mighty vampires employ this Discipline to create sinkholes, collapse unstable sewer tunnels or open up vast caverns in rural areas desperately essential to their descendants. The most outrageous stories concern entire ecosystems based around massive chthonic worms, subterranean leviathans or other burrowers beneath the Earth's crust. Whether this supernatural power (if it exists at all) involves summoning these creatures or merely shifting vast amounts of earth with the power of the mind remains a point of conjecture. Your Storyteller must decide.

System: If these creatures exist, then Nosferatu Ancients can control them somewhat sparingly. A Nosferatu Methuselah should theoretically be able to summon and command a creature once each year for every five points of Willpower (or five Willpower Traits) he possesses. First, the vampire burns these temporary points (or Traits) for a period of at least one month; he cannot regain them until this time has elapsed. The size of the subterranean disturbance depends on a Charisma + Survival roll; the difficulty depends on how rural the chosen location is. (An uninhabited plot of land in the midst of the Sahara would be difficulty 6; downtown Manhattan is difficulty 10.) Storytellers may choose to forego game mechanics where Methuselahs are concerned, of course, and just pass around newspaper clippings of recent massive earthquakes throughout the world.

OBFUSCATE

Obfuscate is the most commonly used Nosferatu Discipline. Many neonates cannot imagine what it would be like to endure immortality without it. Unfortunately, they rarely manage to make full use of it, preferring to blithely wander around the streets unseen, impersonate the occasional mundane mortal and hide from danger whenever it manifests. Take a closer look, and you'll see the power Obfuscate can grant a clever Nosferatu.

Video and Audio Surveillance: Nosferatu specialize in the sale of dirty little secrets. It doesn't take a master of the Obfuscate Discipline to hide in a corner with a video camera or a microphone. All a spy of this type has to do is stay silent and stay in one place. These are exactly the parameters of the Cloak of Shadows Discipline. If a neonate Nosferatu only knows this level of the Obfuscate Discipline, another member of his brood can easily move into position using Cloak the Gathering and rendezvous with him.

Social Chaos: Nosferatu don't have to limit themselves to innocuous personas when using Mask of a Thousand Faces. Many legendary vampires have created chaos by impersonating primogen, princes, mortal celebrities and other well-known individuals. Consider the turmoil that would ensue during a Toreador's love affair with a mortal if his chippie saw him about town with someone else. What if the Brujah elder (or someone who looked just like him) threatened the prince with bodily harm? If a Nosferatu brood isn't treated with respect, the threat of social chaos in the local Camarilla is a potent motivator.

Urban Renewal: Some Nosferatu employ the tactic of "social chaos" in the mortal world as well, especially when they've targeted an entire neighborhood of kine. Creeps know that if a few old buildings are scheduled for demolition or if a house has been condemned, an urban neighborhood can become a haven for Nosferatu above ground. The process takes time, but consider the value of causing a riot in a poor neighborhood, enacting a few atrocities in the guise of a local policeman or taking the place of a local gang leader. If enough horrific acts unleash chaos in a neighborhood, then the chosen locale is one step closer to urban renewal.

Falsified Blackmail: Nosferatu often gain influence over local politicians by blackmailing them with incriminating evidence. Sometimes the evidence isn't even real. Media-savvy Nosferatu have made a thriving trade out of using Mask of a Thousand Faces and a camera. While many are unable to do this with video cameras, the technique works surprisingly well with film. A picture of a local

v.robb ~ 2000

politician performing unspeakable acts with an unknown prostitute, a pornographic picture of a local celebrity or an incriminating snapshot of an ordinary person committing an extraordinary crime can be worth a fortune... even if it's not real.

POTENCE

Prowess, might, vigor, intensity, puissance — no matter what name you describe it with, Potence is an impressive Discipline. Too many neonates think of it as a simple, brutal combat ability, but it is actually much more. It's actually a sophisticated, complex and unpredictable combat ability... coupled with its uses in Nosferatu art and architecture.

Construction: Expanding a city's sewer system takes more than political influence and faithful ghouls. When making improvements to the labyrinthine underworld beneath cities, Nosferatu often use Potence to assist the ghouls with the most difficult tasks. Tunneling through solid rock, moving chunks of rock and concrete or just collapsing a tunnel with a powerful blow are also useful skills in Nosferatu construction.

Destruction: Once a Nosferatu's haven and the domain around it have been constructed, he must immediately think of methods to defend it. A common last-ditch defense involves collapsing carefully chosen hallways to block off an invading force. The same brute strength can also be used to collapse entire buildings above ground. Luring an enemy into an unstable building and collapsing the structural supports is a surefire way to kill even the nastiest supernatural creatures.

Sculpture: Nosferatu art often involves massive pieces of stone and metal. Potence allows Nosferatu to chip marble into statues and bend pieces of iron. While it may seem initially odd to create a Nosferatu with the Performance Ability, it does prove useful in such circumstances.

Wrestling: Titanic strength is even deadlier when the person using it is very skilled. Various legendary Nosferatu have put this talent to their own advantage by combining various styles of wrestling with the might of Potence. Different tactics abound. Some elders brawl with the sportsmanlike maneuvers of Greco-Roman wrestling, but they can't compete with more modern methods. Nosferatu wrestlers of Mexico are well acquainted with the *lucha libre* style, employing it frequently

IMPROVISED WEAPONS FOR POTENCE		
Feat of Strength/difficulty / damage		
Sewer Lid	5	8	6
Thrown Gate	7	8	7
Motorcycle	9	9	8
Compact Car	11	10	9

against other supernatural creatures; there are hundreds of Mexican wrestling films where heroes battle vampires, werewolves or worse.

Hurling Things: Why use your fists to smash your enemies when there are heavier things you can crush them with? Using an appropriate "feat of strength," a Nosferatu can toss iron gates, sewer lids or even compact cars at his opponents. You're never without a weapon when you can rip metal out of a wall. The next section includes some (optional) game mechanics for this tactic.

POTENT COMBAT

In the tabletop version of **Vampire**, massive improvised weapons are unwieldy; throwing an unbalanced, overweight chunk of *anything* usually requires a Dexterity + Athletics or Melee roll; the difficulty should be at least an 8 or 9. Optionally, the chosen target may not be required to make a Willpower roll to "abort to Dodge"; if a frenzying Nosferatu starts to pick up a sports utility vehicle, it may instead require a Willpower roll to do anything *other* than Dodging for cover. Check out the sidebar for a few of the more commonly used weapons.

In the live-action version of the game, as represented by **Mind's Eye Theater**, such feats may be amusing, but should be as difficult as they are ridiculous. Socially roleplaying an interview with a Nosferatu elder should be encouraged; requiring the same player to pant and heave as he lifts the index card for a pickup truck over his head is just plain goofy. Nonetheless, if a player really wants to improvise thrown weapons, the Narrator may want to set up a few prop cards specifically for such eventualities. Any improvised weapon of this sort has the Traits: Unwieldy x 3; this makes hitting someone with such a massive weapon more difficult, but does not reduce the damage it does. To convert damage for improvised weapons, take the number of damage dice and divide it by two. (Or something like that.)

THE NEED TO FEED

Stalking human prey above ground can be particularly difficult for Nosferatu. Humans tend to flee from hideous creatures, especially ones that obviously want to feast on them. The Obfuscate Discipline can help, but not every vampire has it. Few Sewer Rats develop a talent for the Dominate or Presence Disciplines, which are so essential when Ventrue and Toreador feed. Neonate Nosferatu are at an even greater risk, since they don't wield a great deal of supernatural power. Never fear. Not every Nosferatu needs to specialize exclusively in the Obfuscate Discipline to survive. Learning to hunt may be difficult at first, but vampires have centuries to refine their techniques.

Ghouled Slaves: Blood-addicted vitae slaves will do anything to sate the desires of their masters. Some ghouls show their devotion by bringing an occasional meal. By luring the hapless prey into a secretive place, they provide an easy opportunity for a vampire to feed. Why stalk up on prey unseen? The look they get in their eyes as they're about get drained by a hideous monster is as enjoyable as the act of feeding itself.

Blood Dolls: The process of creating a blood doll is fairly simple. Capture a human, ghoul him, and addict him to your blood. Do whatever it takes to keep him around long enough, but nurture his blood bond with care. Once you've won his heart and soul with your precious vitae, you've produced a mortal who will allow you to feed from him regularly. Granted, Nosferatu blood dolls become physically warped and degenerate over time, but some humans will sacrifice anything for love... even their freedom.

Quell the Beast: This Animalism Discipline works on any sentient creature, including humans. A bestial Nosferatu can decide to repeatedly stalk the same alleyway or street corner, lulling victims into a pacified trance. Remember the scene in a horror movie where a curious teenager wanders into a place he obviously shouldn't go? No sane person would every venture into the basement of a deserted house or investigate a sewer grate thrown suspiciously wide open... unless they got a little psychic "push," perhaps. Repeated exposure to Quell the Beast can actually be addictive. Victims keep coming back to the same deserted alleyway over and over, returning with hazy memories of the ecstasy of the Kiss.

Sandmen: Elders scorn the thought of feeding off sleeping prey. It's too damn simple! A stealthy vampire, however, may come to prefer the thrill of sneaking into a victim's house at night. Legends of vampires needing to be invited into someone's home are a perfect bit of misinformation. Just in case, make sure you plan your escape route carefully. Not every home has a convenient sewer grate nearby.

Thugs: A Nosferatu's command of the Potence Discipline offers a far more brutal version of hunting. A thug who can knock a victim unconscious with a single blow can carry his prey away and feed at his leisure. Setting up the ambush is a little tricky, but patience pays off. Failed Sandmen sometimes learn to just smash down a door and take what they want.

Bogeymen: Feeding off children is a particularly vile way to survive, but needs must as the devil drives. Whether out of cowardice or preference, such creatures are responsible for countless legends of monsters lurking in wait for bad little children. When kids are scared out of their wits, parents are quick to disbelieve obviously delusional stories of what their predators looked like....

The Internet: We don't need to go into too much detail here. Suffice to say that over the 'Net, no one needs to see your face. Gathering all the information you can about a potential victim, from his official records to the secrets he betrays in an Internet chat room, can greatly aid your chances in finding an ideal candidate for thralldom, the Embrace or an occasional late-night snack. It's as creepy as it is effective.

Pack Tactics: When all other methods of stalking prey fail, never forget the usefulness of hunting in a pack. Whether you decide to spend your evenings in a Camarilla coterie, set out into the city as part of a Nosferatu brood or abandon all caution to run through the streets with an inhuman Sabbat pack, teamwork pays off. Jaded vampires sometimes devise elaborate strategies for flushing prey from their protective cover, tracking them through the streets and sharing in the kill at the end of a job well done.

CHAPTER THREE: NOSFERATU CHARACTERS

Man delights not me.
— William Shakespeare, *Hamlet*

HERE THERE BE MONSTERS

Every Nosferatu is unique, but a few archetypes resurface again and again. The names, faces and backgrounds may change, but by any other name, the foul essence of Clan Nosferatu remains the same. To help you fill the sewers, slums and cesspools of your cities, we've included a few examples of the despicable monsters this clan has to offer. Customize their back stories, throw in a good dose of indulgent roleplaying, and you'll be ready to trudge through the sewers in two shakes of a rat's tail.

CLEOPATRA

Quote: *I'll be out in a minute… I just need to fix my face….*

Prelude: Once you were beautiful, but such beauty breeds envy in others. There was a time when men longed to possess you. Women longed to *be* you. Then an absolute beast ravished and destroyed you. He came to you in the guise of a handsome stranger, but when he finally got you alone, you found out he was just like all the others: a monster deep inside.

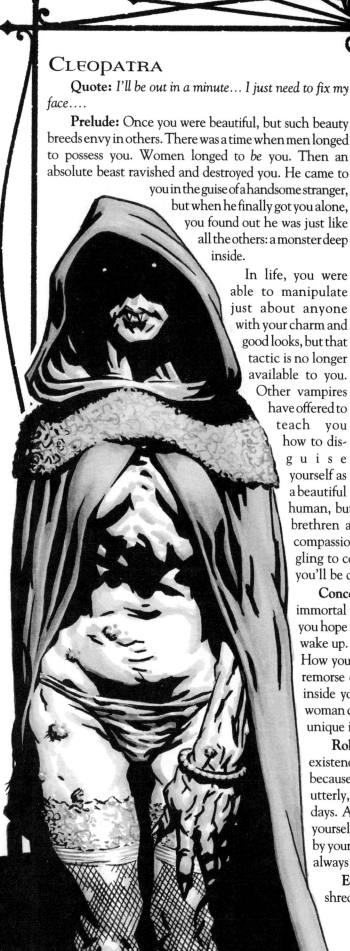

In life, you were able to manipulate just about anyone with your charm and good looks, but that tactic is no longer available to you. Other vampires have offered to teach you how to disguise yourself as a beautiful human, but the idea sickens you. Although you and your Nosferatu brethren are truly hideous, you are just beginning to understand compassion, sympathy and the pangs of conscience. You are struggling to comprehend something deeper in your soul; unless you do, you'll be doomed to mourn your lost beauty for all eternity.

Concept: You're a beautiful woman trapped in the body of an immortal monster. Every evening, when you arise from a deep sleep, you hope that your horrible recurrent dream will end and you'll finally wake up. Yet every night, the nightmare begins again the same way. How you'll react to this sudden change — with bitterness, extreme remorse or perhaps even cunning — depends on what lies deeper inside you. As someone intensely aware of how a vain and petty woman can get by on appearances, you've also got very thorough and unique insights into human (and vampiric) psychology.

Roleplaying Hints: You have a choice. You can return to the existence you had before, fooling others into thinking you are special because you can mirror beauty. Or, if you like, you can reject that utterly, trying to develop qualities you never had in your breathing days. Among your own kind, you have no choice but to present yourself as the person you really are. Other Nosferatu aren't fooled by your pretense at wit or sophistication. You are a monster and will always be one until you can earn the respect of other vampires.

Equipment: fashionable purse, make-up case, black lipstick, shredded lingerie, broken mirror, exquisite clothes, pepper spray

---

VAMPIRE THE MASQUERADE

NAME:	NATURE: Penitent	GENERATION: 11th
PLAYER:	DEMEANOR: Child	HAVEN:
CHRONICLE:	CLAN: Nosferatu	CONCEPT: Cleopatra

ATTRIBUTES

PHYSICAL		SOCIAL		MENTAL	
Strength	●●○○○	Charisma	●●●●●	Perception	●●●●○
Dexterity	●●○○○	Manipulation	●●●●●	Intelligence	●●●○○
Stamina	●●○○○	Appearance	○○○○○	Wits	●●○○○

ABILITIES

TALENTS		SKILLS		KNOWLEDGES	
Alertness	●○○○○	Animal Ken	○○○○○	Academics	●○○○○
Athletics	○○○○○	Crafts	●●○○○	Computer	●○○○○
Brawl	○○○○○	Drive	●○○○○	Finance	●●○○○
Dodge	●○○○○	Etiquette	●●●●○	Investigation	●●○○○
Empathy	●●○○○	Firearms	●●○○○	Law	○○○○○
Expression	●○○○○	Melee	○○○○○	Linguistics	○○○○○
Intimidation	●●○○○	Performance	●●●●○	Medicine	○○○○○
Leadership	○○○○○	Security	○○○○○	Occult	○○○○○
Streetwise	●●○○○	Stealth	●●●○○	Politics	●○○○○
Subterfuge	●●●○○	Survival	●○○○○	Science	○○○○○

ADVANTAGES

BACKGROUNDS		DISCIPLINES		VIRTUES	
Generation	●●○○○	Obfuscate	●●●○○	Conscience/Conviction	●●●○○
Herd	●●○○○		○○○○○		
Resources	●●●○○		○○○○○	Self-Control/Instinct	●●●●●
	○○○○○		○○○○○		
	○○○○○		○○○○○		
	○○○○○		○○○○○	Courage	●●●○○

MERITS/FLAWS

HUMANITY/PATH
●●●●●●●○○○

WILLPOWER
●●●●○○○○○○
□□□□□□□□□□

BLOOD POOL
□□□□□□□□□□
□□□□□□□□□□

HEALTH

Bruised		□
Hurt	-1	□
Injured	-1	□
Wounded	-2	□
Mauled	-2	□
Crippled	-5	□
Incapacitated		□

EXPERIENCE

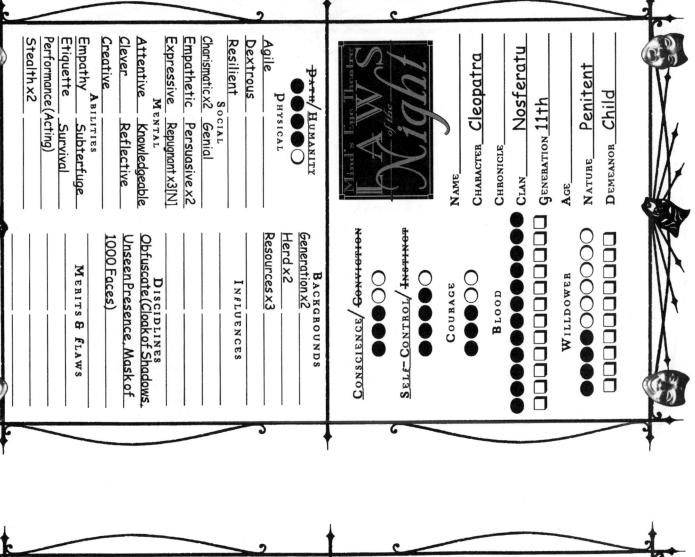

Mind's Eye Theatre — LAWS of the Night (top sheet)

NAME _____
CHARACTER __Cleopatra__
CHRONICLE _____
CLAN __Nosferatu__
GENERATION __11th__
AGE _____
NATURE __Penitent__
DEMEANOR __Child__

CONSCIENCE/CONVICTION
SELF-CONTROL/INSTINCT
COURAGE
BLOOD
WILLPOWER

PATH/HUMANITY

PHYSICAL
- Agile
- Dextrous
- Resilient

SOCIAL
- Charismatic x2 Genial
- Empathetic Persuasive x2
- Expressive Repugnant x3 [N]

MENTAL
- Attentive Knowledgeable
- Clever Reflective
- Creative

ABILITIES
- Empathy Subterfuge
- Etiquette Survival
- Performance (Acting)
- Stealth x2

BACKGROUNDS
- Generation x2
- Herd x2
- Resources x3

INFLUENCES

DISCIPLINES
- Obfuscate (Cloak of Shadows, Unseen Presence, Mask of 1000 Faces)

MERITS & FLAWS

Mind's Eye Theatre — LAWS of the Night (bottom sheet)

NAME _____
CHARACTER __Advisor__
CHRONICLE _____
CLAN __Nosferatu__
GENERATION __13th__
AGE _____
NATURE __Director__
DEMEANOR __Conformist__

CONSCIENCE/CONVICTION
SELF-CONTROL/INSTINCT
COURAGE
BLOOD
WILLPOWER

PATH/HUMANITY

PHYSICAL
- Enduring
- Nimble
- Wiry

SOCIAL
- Charming Persuasive x2
- Dignified Repugnant x3 [N]
- Diplomatic

MENTAL
- Alert Patient
- Knowledgeable x2 Shrewd
- Insightful

ABILITIES
- Dodge Politics
- Etiquette Stealth
- Expression Subterfuge
- Finance Survival

BACKGROUNDS
- Contacts x2
- Resources x2
- Retainers x1

INFLUENCES

DISCIPLINES
- Obfuscate (Cloak of Shadows, Unseen Presence, Mask of 1000 Faces)
- Presence (Awe)

MERITS & FLAWS

Advisor

Quote: *Yes, sir... No, sir... Well, sir, a stake through the heart sounds like a good idea, but wouldn't flaying his skin be a bit more effective? Yes, I'll put someone right on that, sir....*

Prelude: You never amounted to much in life. While you had a talent for diplomacy and demonstrated fabulous "people skills," you also had a bad habit of propping up other people's authority. You never had the drive to become a charismatic leader. You were content to be a toady, a flunky, the man behind the scenes who drew a steady paycheck and let others seize his share of fame and fortune.

You must have done something right, though, because you were recruited into the world of the undead. Thanks to the Embrace, you're immortal, potent and supernatural... and nothing much has changed. You've started cowering behind a "vampire prince," giving him advice on all sorts of bizarre night-to-night events. You also act as a sort of "manager" for other Nosferatu, implementing the prince's policies. The prince takes the credit for your ideas, but somehow, you feel safer standing behind him than in front of him. After all, the princes of the world come and go, but toadying yes-men never seem to go out of style.

Concept: You have the prince's ear, and for some reason you cannot fathom, he actually trusts you. Occasionally, he confides in you. Maybe it's because you have ties to others of your kind, skulking creatures even more hideous than you. They keep you far more informed than the egotistical prince you prop up, and in exchange, you bring them choice tidbits of news from the prince's chambers.

Roleplaying Hints: Why take risks by being the man in charge? Ride on his coattails, and exploit the situation for all you can get. Hide behind a politician with power and promise, convince him that he can't get by without your skills, bow and scrape like a stooge, and stick by him to the end... at least, until he fails and you have to shop your skills to someone else. Your survival depends on your chosen victim's success. As long as you stay on the good side of people in power, no doubt you'll be safe. Just make sure your tongue doesn't get too black when you're licking the prince's boots....

Equipment: cell phone, Brioni business suit, laptop computer, three handkerchiefs (for mopping up the pus you ooze from time to time), a tin of shoe polish

VAMPIRE
THE MASQUERADE

NAME:	NATURE: Director	GENERATION: 13th
PLAYER:	DEMEANOR: Conformist	HAVEN:
CHRONICLE:	CLAN: Nosferatu	CONCEPT: Advisor

ATTRIBUTES

Physical		Social		Mental	
Strength	●●○○○	Charisma	●●●●○	Perception	●●●●●
Dexterity	●●○○○	Manipulation	●●●●○	Intelligence	●●●●○
Stamina	●●○○○	Appearance	○○○○○	Wits	●●●○○

ABILITIES

Talents		Skills		Knowledges	
Alertness	●●○○○	Animal Ken	○○○○○	Academics	●●○○○
Athletics	○○○○○	Crafts	●○○○○	Computer	●○○○○
Brawl	○○○○○	Drive	○○○○○	Finance	●●●○○
Dodge	●●●○○	Etiquette	●●●○○	Investigation	●●○○○
Empathy	●●○○○	Firearms	○○○○○	Law	○○○○○
Expression	●●●○○	Melee	○○○○○	Linguistics	○○○○○
Intimidation	○○○○○	Performance	●○○○○	Medicine	○○○○○
Leadership	●○○○○	Security	○○○○○	Occult	○○○○○
Streetwise	○○○○○	Stealth	●○○○○	Politics	●●●○○
Subterfuge	●●●○○	Survival	○○○○○	Science	○○○○○

ADVANTAGES

Backgrounds		Disciplines		Virtues	
Contacts	●●○○○	Obfuscate	●●●○○	Conscience/Conviction	●●●●○
Resources	●●○○○	Presence	●○○○○		
Retainers	●○○○○		○○○○○		
	○○○○○		○○○○○	Self-Control/Instinct	●●●●○
	○○○○○		○○○○○		
	○○○○○		○○○○○	Courage	●●○○○

Merits/Flaws	Humanity/Path	Health	
	●●●●●●●●○○	Bruised	☐
		Hurt -1	☐
		Injured -1	☐
	Willpower	Wounded -2	☐
	●●●●○○○○○○	Mauled -2	☐
	☐☐☐☐☐☐☐☐☐☐	Crippled -5	☐
		Incapacitated	☐
	Blood Pool	Experience	
	☐☐☐☐☐☐☐☐☐☐		
	☐☐☐☐☐☐☐☐☐☐		

LEATHERFACE

Quote: *You remind me of my mother. I never really liked my mother....*

Prelude: Humans are such easy prey. You hated them all when you were alive, and you hate them even more now that you are dead. In vampiric society, you go through the motions of being civilized, but when you have the chance to stalk human beings, the urges of the Beast overtake you. Why take just a little blood when you hunt? Take their lives instead.

Other vampires — especially Nosferatu — must not learn who you really are or what you have done. If they learn that your soul is as repulsive as your flesh, they'll destroy you immediately. Even the Sabbat wouldn't understand your little hobbies. Since even the Creeps have to remain hidden, they wouldn't like an obsessive killer stirring up the local kine. You must work especially hard to show that you are an upstanding member of vampiric society and struggle tirelessly to support your brood. Once you've done that, you've earned the privilege to let the Beast within you roam free. Rack up a body count, and hide the bodies well.

Concept: All vampires are predatory creatures; you're just better at stalking and killing than most of them. Occasionally, you are very ruthless but not enough to reveal your true nature. Each session, while you hunt, you must do so in secret. (Note to the Storyteller: Each session, the player roleplaying this character should write you a note describing his character's atrocities for the session. Play them out in a "secret conference" if you like, and keep those Morality rolls secret.)

Roleplaying Hints: If you feel inexorably drawn to playing a vampiric serial killer, you probably don't need advice from us. However, if you've get stuck, do what any great Leatherface would do: Study the masters. Bookstores are filled with tales of true crime — what motivates a Gacy, Bundy, Dahmer or Klebold? What makes people like that break down? If your head starts to ache too much from it all, snap your character back into its alternate personality: That carefully maintained façade is essential to your monster's sanity.

Equipment: nondescript (but absolutely filthy) clothing, icepick, blowtorch, run-down van (with malfunctioning seat belts and door locks), surgical table with restraints

VAMPIRE THE MASQUERADE

NAME: NATURE: Monster   GENERATION: 9th
PLAYER: DEMEANOR: Conformist   HAVEN:
CHRONICLE: CLAN: Nosferatu   CONCEPT: Leatherface

ATTRIBUTES

Physical		Social		Mental	
Strength	●●●○○	Charisma	●●○○○	Perception	●●●○○
Dexterity	●●●○○	Manipulation	●●●○○	Intelligence	●●○○○
Stamina	●●●●○	Appearance	○○○○○	Wits	●●●○○

ABILITIES

Talents		Skills		Knowledges	
Alertness	●○○○○	Animal Ken	○○○○○	Academics	○○○○○
Athletics	●●○○○	Crafts	○○○○○	Computer	○○○○○
Brawl	●●●○○	Drive	○○○○○	Finance	○○○○○
Dodge	●●○○○	Etiquette	○○○○○	Investigation	●●○○○
Empathy	○○○○○	Firearms	○○○○○	Law	●○○○○
Expression	○○○○○	Melee	●●●○○	Linguistics	○○○○○
Intimidation	●●○○○	Performance	○○○○○	Medicine	○○○○○
Leadership	○○○○○	Security	●○○○○	Occult	●●○○○
Streetwise	○○○○○	Stealth	●●●○○	Politics	○○○○○
Subterfuge	●●○○○	Survival	●●○○○	Science	○○○○○

ADVANTAGES

Backgrounds		Disciplines		Virtues	
Fame	●○○○○	Fortitude	●○○○○	Conscience/~~Conviction~~	●●●●○
Generation	●●●●○	Obfuscate	●●○○○		
	○○○○○	Potence	●○○○○		
	○○○○○		○○○○○	Self-Control/~~Instinct~~	●○○○○
	○○○○○		○○○○○		
	○○○○○		○○○○○		
	○○○○○		○○○○○	Courage	●●●●●

MERITS/FLAWS

HUMANITY/PATH
●●●●●○○○○○

WILLPOWER
●●●●●●○○○○
□□□□□□□□□□

HEALTH

Bruised		□
Hurt	-1	□
Injured	-1	□
Wounded	-2	□
Mauled	-2	□
Crippled	-5	□
Incapacitated		□

BLOOD POOL

EXPERIENCE

Character Sheet 1

Name: _____
Character: Leatherface
Chronicle: _____
Clan: Nosferatu
Generation: 9th
Age: _____
Nature: Monster
Demeanor: Conformist

Conscience/Conviction: ●●○○
Self-Control/Instinct: ●●●○
Courage: ●●●
Blood: ●●●●●●●●●●
Willpower: ●●●●●●○○

Backgrounds
Fame x1
Generation x4

Influences

Disciplines
Fortitude (Endurance)
Obfuscate (Cloak of Shadows)
Unseen Presence
Potence (Prowess)

Merits & Flaws

Path/Humanity: ○○

Physical
Brawny x2   Tireless
Ferocious x2   Vigorous
Tenacious

Social
Intimidating x2
Repugnant x3[N]

Mental
Wily
Alert
Attentive
Cunning x2

Abilities
Brawl   Occult
Dodge   Stealth x2
Investigation   Survival
Melee

Character Sheet 2

Name: _____
Character: Initiate Loremaster
Chronicle: _____
Clan: Nosferatu
Generation: 11th
Age: _____
Nature: Perfectionist
Demeanor: Pedagogue

Conscience/Conviction: ●●○
Self-Control/Instinct: ●●●
Courage: ●●○
Blood: ●●●●●●●●●●●●
Willpower: ●●●○○○

Backgrounds
Contacts x2
Generation x2

Influences
Occult x2
Retainer x1

Disciplines
Animalism (Feral Whispers)
Obfuscate (Cloak of Shadows)
Unseen Presence
Potence (Prowess)

Merits & Flaws

Path/Humanity: ○●●●

Physical
Agile
Enduring
Tireless

Social
Diplomatic   Genial
Eloquent   Ingratiating
Expressive   Repugnant x3[N]

Mental
Discerning   Knowledgeable x2
Disciplined   Wise
Insightful x2

Abilities
Academics   Stealth
Lore (Kindrd)   Subterfuge
Occult
Survival
Science (Biology)

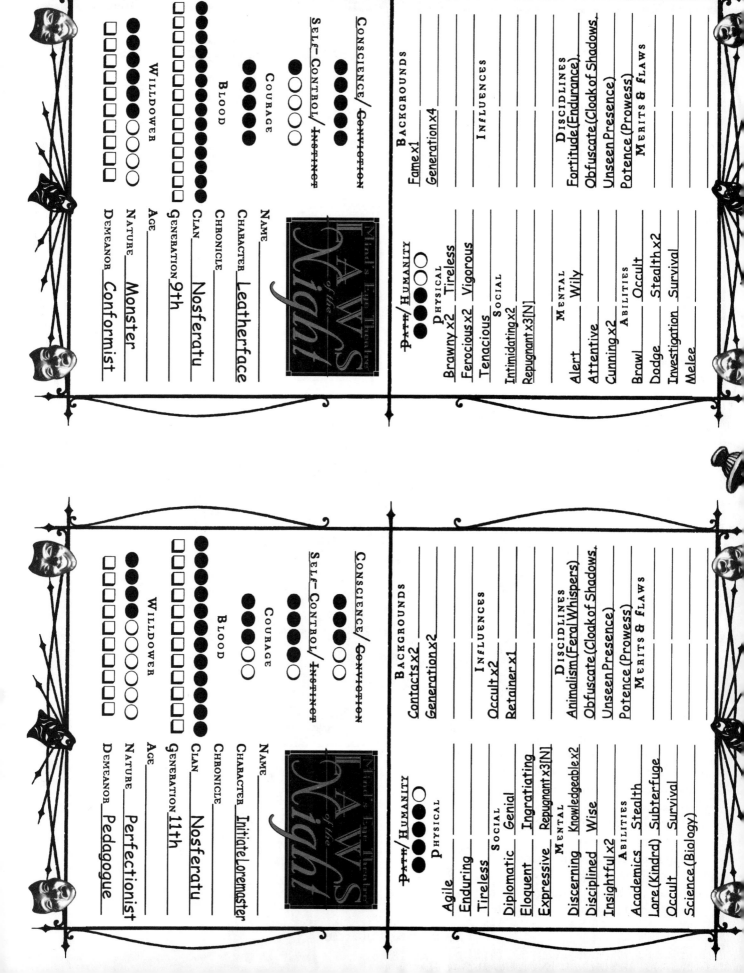

INITIATE LOREMASTER

Quote: *There are things in this world man was not meant to know. Fortunately, I am no longer a man....*

Prelude: Before your Embrace, you tried to make a living out of studying the occult. You desperately tried to unearth the secrets of the universe... and it was pathetic. Finding an employer who recognized your specialty as a legitimate, marketable skill was nearly impossible. You scraped by while writing watered-down New Age paperbacks, Time-Life books of the supernatural and the occasional comic-book script. Of course, you leaked just enough of the Truth to attract the attention of the *real* supernatural world, and you've been studying it ever since from behind the scenes.

Since you were forcibly abducted into the world of vampires, you have been consistently amazed by how many other monsters stalk the night. Most Nosferatu do a brisk trade exchanging the secrets of Kindred society, but you hate having so much competition. If you're going to make a business out of this, you might as well deal in rare and expensive merchandise. You've carefully sought out myths and legends about other supernatural creatures. Who gives a damn which mortal the prince is screwing this month? There are far more fascinating truths lurking in the night.

Concept: During character creation, you must choose for this character one specialty in the Occult Ability. While you're well versed on a wide array of esoteric topics, you're particularly good with that one. On the one hand, your character knows far more about it than most Kindred; on the other, if you gave away the darkest secrets of their societies, you'd be out of business in a heartbeat (if you had such a thing).

Roleplaying Hints: You pride yourself on being professional. Because you must trade with a wide range of supernatural beasties, diplomacy is essential to your business. While you spend a great deal of time consorting with other vampires, you receive visitors every night who wish to consult with you on your very specialized fields of knowledge. You prefer to hide your grotesque appearance as much as possible, but if you need to press a point, it does serve as an indelible reminder of the presence of the occult in the world.

Equipment: silver key to your private library and office, Victorian suit, antique fountain pen, various pieces of correspondence, valuable leather-bound tome

VAMPIRE THE MASQUERADE

NAME:
PLAYER:
CHRONICLE:

NATURE: Perfectionist
DEMEANOR: Pedagogue
CLAN: Nosferatu

GENERATION: 11th
HAVEN:
CONCEPT: Initiate Loremaster

ATTRIBUTES

Physical		Social		Mental	
Strength	●○○○○	Charisma	●●●●○	Perception	●●●○○
Dexterity	●○○○○	Manipulation	●●●○○	Intelligence	●●●●○
Stamina	●●●○○	Appearance	○○○○○	Wits	●●●○○

ABILITIES

Talents		Skills		Knowledges	
Alertness	●●○○○	Animal Ken	●●○○○	Academics	●●●○○
Athletics	○○○○○	Crafts	●○○○○	Computer	○○○○○
Brawl	○○○○○	Drive	○○○○○	Finance	○○○○○
Dodge	●○○○○	Etiquette	●●○○○	Investigation	●●○○○
Empathy	●●○○○	Firearms	○○○○○	Law	●○○○○
Expression	●●○○○	Melee	○○○○○	Linguistics	●○○○○
Intimidation	○○○○○	Performance	○○○○○	Medicine	○○○○○
Leadership	○○○○○	Security	○○○○○	Occult	●●●○○
Streetwise	○○○○○	Stealth	●○○○○	Politics	○○○○○
Subterfuge	●●●○○	Survival	○○○○○	Science	●●●○○

ADVANTAGES

Backgrounds		Disciplines		Virtues	
Contacts	●●○○○	Animalism	●○○○○	Conscience/Conviction	●●●○○
Generation	●●○○○	Obfuscate	●●●○○		
Resources	●●○○○	Potence	●○○○○		
Retainers	●○○○○		○○○○○	Self-Control/Instinct	●●●●●○
	○○○○○		○○○○○		
	○○○○○		○○○○○		
	○○○○○		○○○○○	Courage	●●●○○

MERITS/FLAWS

HUMANITY/PATH
●●●●●●●○○○

WILLPOWER
●●●●●○○○○○
□□□□□□□□□□

BLOOD POOL
□□□□□□□□□□
□□□□□□□□□□

HEALTH
Bruised		□
Hurt	-1	□
Injured	-1	□
Wounded	-2	□
Mauled	-2	□
Crippled	-5	□
Incapacitated		□

EXPERIENCE

RESEARCH SPECIALIST

Quote: *Hrrm. Hrrm. An undeniable statistical correlation between crop circles in Indiana and cattle mutilations in the Chicago stockyards. Fuel up the van. We've got to go get some samples....*

Prelude: You uncover secrets no one else will believe. When the doors of the library close at night, you go to work. While the ghoul janitor tends to the maintenance of your little kingdom, you have hours of quiet isolation, reflection and study.

Other vampires travel to Tremere chantries for consultations on the occult, but you are methodical in tracking down clues and hints of supernatural activity hidden in the mortal world.

Now a coterie of Kindred is offering you a chance to venture further away from your private sanctum. They seem to value you for your keen mind and want your aid investigating supernatural phenomena throughout the city. One night, you're lurking outside the park where werewolves make their home; the next, you're tailing the Brujah elder to find out about his secret political contacts. No matter what you observe, you conclude each evening with the same solitary activity: retreating back into the library to peruse the news for more leads.

Concept: You have a gift for sorting through news of mortal events and finding hints of supernatural involvement. Other Kindred are fooled by the façades of the Masquerade, but like others of your clan, you aren't tricked by mere appearances. You value the solitary time you spend in your haven; you just happen to spend it enraptured by esoteric works of reference. When you're certain that your investigation has revealed the presence of the occult, you rush to your coterie to ask for their help in studying the problem further. In return for their help, you support them with your investigative skills from time to time.

Roleplaying Hints: When presented with a mystery that involves something other than vampiric society, you are tenacious, risking everything to understand the unknown. For some reason, it distracts you from having to cope with the fact that you, yourself, are a monster, an anomaly that doesn't belong in this world. Keep searching.

Equipment: key to the library (and the tunnels beneath it), copious notes, spare notepad, camera with film, private stash of newspapers and tabloids

---

VAMPIRE: THE MASQUERADE

NAME:	**NATURE:** Judge	**GENERATION:** 12th
PLAYER:	**DEMEANOR:** Fanatic	**HAVEN:**
CHRONICLE:	**CLAN:** Nosferatu	**CONCEPT:** Research Specialist

ATTRIBUTES

PHYSICAL	SOCIAL	MENTAL
Strength ●●○○○	Charisma ●○○○○	Perception ●●●●○
Dexterity ●●●○○	Manipulation ●●●●○	Intelligence ●●●●○
Stamina ●●○○○	Appearance ○○○○○	Wits ●●●○○

ABILITIES

TALENTS	SKILLS	KNOWLEDGES
Alertness ●●○○○	Animal Ken ○○○○○	Academics ●●●●○
Athletics ○○○○○	Crafts ●●○○○	Computer ●●○○○
Brawl ○○○○○	Drive ●○○○○	Finance ○○○○○
Dodge ●●○○○	Etiquette ●○○○○	Investigation ●●●○○
Empathy ●○○○○	Firearms ●●○○○	Law ○○○○○
Expression ●●○○○	Melee ○○○○○	Linguistics ○○○○○
Intimidation ○○○○○	Performance ●○○○○	Medicine ●○○○○
Leadership ○○○○○	Security ●●○○○	Occult ●●○○○
Streetwise ●○○○○	Stealth ●●○○○	Politics ○○○○○
Subterfuge ○○○○○	Survival ●●○○○	Science ●○○○○

ADVANTAGES

BACKGROUNDS	DISCIPLINES	VIRTUES
Allies ●○○○○	Obfuscate ●●○○○	Conscience/Conviction ●●●○○
Contacts ●●○○○	Potence ●○○○○	
Generation ●●○○○	○○○○○	
Retainers ●●○○○	○○○○○	Self-Control/Instinct ●●●○○
○○○○○	○○○○○	
○○○○○	○○○○○	
○○○○○	○○○○○	Courage ●●●●●

MERITS/FLAWS

HUMANITY/PATH ●●●●●●○○○○

WILLPOWER ●●●●○○○○○○ □□□□□□□□□□

BLOOD POOL □□□□□□□□□□ □□□□□□□□□□

HEALTH

Bruised		□
Hurt	-1	□
Injured	-1	□
Wounded	-2	□
Mauled	-2	□
Crippled	-5	□
Incapacitated		□

EXPERIENCE

LEIF JONES 2000

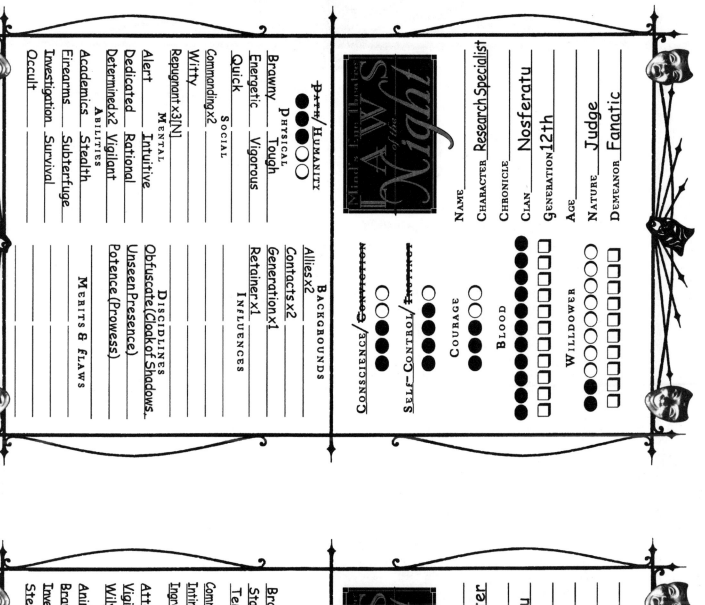

Mind's Eye Theatre — LAWS of the Night

Character Sheet 1

NAME _____
CHARACTER Research Specialist
CHRONICLE _____
CLAN Nosferatu
GENERATION 12th
AGE _____
NATURE Judge
DEMEANOR Fanatic

CONSCIENCE/~~Conviction~~
SELF-CONTROL/~~Instinct~~
COURAGE
BLOOD
WILLPOWER

PATH/HUMANITY

PHYSICAL
Brawny _____ Tough _____
Energetic _____ Vigorous _____
Quick _____

SOCIAL
Commanding x2 _____
Witty _____
Repugnant x3 [N] _____

MENTAL
Alert _____ Intuitive _____
Dedicated _____ Rational _____
Determined x2 _____ Vigilant _____

ABILITIES
Academics _____ Stealth _____
Firearms _____ Subterfuge _____
Investigation _____ Survival _____
Occult _____

BACKGROUNDS
Allies x2 _____
Contacts x2 _____
Generation x1 _____
Retainer x1 _____

INFLUENCES

DISCIPLINES
Obfuscate (Cloak of Shadows,
Unseen Presence)
Potence (Prowess)

MERITS & FLAWS

Character Sheet 2

NAME _____
CHARACTER Hive Master
CHRONICLE _____
CLAN Nosferatu
GENERATION 13th
AGE _____
NATURE Deviant
DEMEANOR Loner

CONSCIENCE/~~Conviction~~
SELF-CONTROL/~~Instinct~~
COURAGE
BLOOD
WILLPOWER

PATH/HUMANITY

PHYSICAL
Brawny x2 _____ Wiry _____
Stalwart _____
Tenacious _____

SOCIAL
Commanding x3 _____ Repugnant x3 [N] _____
Intimidating x2 _____
Ingratiating x2 _____

MENTAL
Attentive _____
Vigilant _____
Wily _____

ABILITIES
Animal Ken _____ Survival x2 _____
Brawl _____
Investigation _____
Stealth _____

BACKGROUNDS
Herd x4 _____
Retainers x1 _____

INFLUENCES

DISCIPLINES
Animalism (Feral Whispers,
The Beckoning, Quell the
Beast, Subsume the Spirit)

MERITS & FLAWS

Hive Master

Quote: ZZZZZZZzzzzz! (pretty! pretty! pretty!) ZzzzzzZZZZZZZ!

Prelude: The Embrace shattered your mind, erasing the memory of your mortal life. You skulked down into the sewers and stayed there. Now you wait at the center of a swarm, sending out your beasts to gather everything you need. Instead of learning to disguise yourself as a mortal or hide from sight, you found companionship in the other creatures of the underworld. Unfortunately, you have great trouble interacting with other societies, whether mortal, supernatural or vampiric, so when you do, you prefer to use your animal allies as intermediaries.

By specializing in the Animalism Discipline, you can dominate an animal and use him to spy for you. Because you are a Nosferatu, though, animals controlled with your supernatural power turn vicious over time. Some even become physically degenerate. Such creatures are shunned by others of their kind (just like you) and come shambling back to the spawning pool you maintain so rigorously. No matter. Hundreds of others are breeding down there, developing an addiction to their master's blood. It's time to take one of them out for a walk.

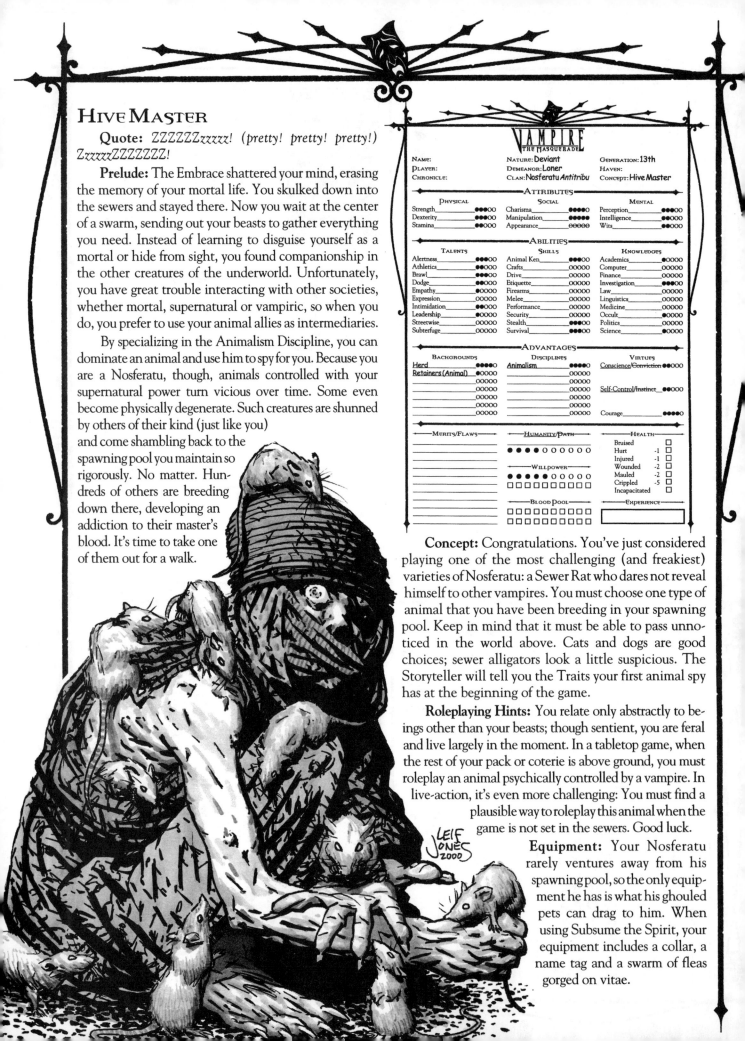

VAMPIRE — THE MASQUERADE

NAME: NATURE: **Deviant**   GENERATION: **13th**
PLAYER: DEMEANOR: **Loner**   HAVEN:
CHRONICLE: CLAN: **Nosferatu Antitribu**   CONCEPT: **Hive Master**

ATTRIBUTES

PHYSICAL
Strength ●●●○○
Dexterity ●●●○○
Stamina ●●○○○

SOCIAL
Charisma ●●●●○
Manipulation ●●●●●
Appearance ⊘⊘⊘⊘⊘

MENTAL
Perception ●●●○○
Intelligence ●●○○○
Wits ●●○○○

ABILITIES

TALENTS
Alertness ●●●○○
Athletics ●●○○○
Brawl ●●●○○
Dodge ●●○○○
Empathy ●○○○○
Expression ○○○○○
Intimidation ●●○○○
Leadership ●○○○○
Streetwise ○○○○○
Subterfuge ○○○○○

SKILLS
Animal Ken ●●●○○
Crafts ○○○○○
Drive ○○○○○
Etiquette ○○○○○
Firearms ○○○○○
Melee ○○○○○
Performance ○○○○○
Security ○○○○○
Stealth ●●●○○
Survival ●●●○○

KNOWLEDGES
Academics ●○○○○
Computer ○○○○○
Finance ○○○○○
Investigation ●●●○○
Law ○○○○○
Linguistics ○○○○○
Medicine ○○○○○
Occult ●○○○○
Politics ○○○○○
Science ●○○○○

ADVANTAGES

BACKGROUNDS
Herd ●●●●○
Retainers (Animal) ●○○○○
_____ ○○○○○
_____ ○○○○○
_____ ○○○○○
_____ ○○○○○
_____ ○○○○○

DISCIPLINES
Animalism ●●●●○
_____ ○○○○○
_____ ○○○○○
_____ ○○○○○
_____ ○○○○○
_____ ○○○○○
_____ ○○○○○

VIRTUES
Conscience/Conviction ●●○○○

Self-Control/Instinct ●●○○○

Courage ●●●●○

MERITS/FLAWS
_____
_____
_____
_____
_____
_____

HUMANITY/PATH
●●●●○○○○○○

WILLPOWER
●●●●●○○○○○
□□□□□□□□□□

BLOOD POOL
□□□□□□□□□□
□□□□□□□□□□

HEALTH
Bruised □
Hurt -1 □
Injured -1 □
Wounded -2 □
Mauled -2 □
Crippled -5 □
Incapacitated □

EXPERIENCE

Concept: Congratulations. You've just considered playing one of the most challenging (and freakiest) varieties of Nosferatu: a Sewer Rat who dares not reveal himself to other vampires. You must choose one type of animal that you have been breeding in your spawning pool. Keep in mind that it must be able to pass unnoticed in the world above. Cats and dogs are good choices; sewer alligators look a little suspicious. The Storyteller will tell you the Traits your first animal spy has at the beginning of the game.

Roleplaying Hints: You relate only abstractly to beings other than your beasts; though sentient, you are feral and live largely in the moment. In a tabletop game, when the rest of your pack or coterie is above ground, you must roleplay an animal psychically controlled by a vampire. In live-action, it's even more challenging: You must find a plausible way to roleplay this animal when the game is not set in the sewers. Good luck.

Equipment: Your Nosferatu rarely ventures away from his spawning pool, so the only equipment he has is what his ghouled pets can drag to him. When using Subsume the Spirit, your equipment includes a collar, a name tag and a swarm of fleas gorged on vitae.

SKIN

Quote: *Remember me? We were at that delightful gallery opening a few weeks ago. You told such wonderful tales of the Old Country. Say, do be a doll and help get past this bouncer, will you?*

Prelude: You hate yourself and what you have become, so you've learned to specialize in being other people. Back in the limelight of your mortal days, you always wanted to be an actor, but you never made it farther than a few drama classes. You jumped from job to job, but each time, you never really felt comfortable revealing how you felt to your co-workers. Instead, you lied frequently, fabricating a false past and pretending you knew more about various subjects than you really did.

Eventually, you moved to another city, hoping to escape from the tangle of lies you had made out of your life, but lying to people gave you an adrenaline rush unlike anything else. Someone must have been watching over your shoulder because he decided to curse you with a true identity that was almost impossible to escape. Now you're an unspeakably hideous monster, but because you can impersonate others with your supernatural abilities, you've finally become a consummate actor. You'll be pursuing a wide variety of roles until the end of time... or until you get caught.

Concept: You're a scam artist skilled at impersonation. Creeping around while invisible will eventually get other neonates in trouble, but you choose to hide in plain sight. You lead a double life, mingling with the vampires of one society while secretly informing another. You are a vital piece of your conspiracy's information network. Whatever you do, don't get caught.

Roleplaying Hints: Your coterie, pack or brood will probably want you to impersonate a wide variety of mortals. Make the most of this. Use your alternate personas to spread chaos and confusion, as much as you can get away with. You can do an amazing imitation of the prince, the leader of a local gang, an up-and-coming politician — just about anything with enough preparation. As long as you don't have to be yourself, you are Everyman... or, at least, every man's nightmare.

Equipment: Your haven includes a trunk filled with various props for your favorite roles. It's also got a big album of photos from your previous life... and you've cut your face out of every one.

VAMPIRE — THE MASQUERADE

NAME:
PLAYER:
CHRONICLE:

NATURE: Loner
DEMEANOR: Trickster
CLAN: Nosferatu

GENERATION: 12th
HAVEN:
CONCEPT: Skin

ATTRIBUTES

PHYSICAL
Strength ●●○○○
Dexterity ●●○○○
Stamina ●●○○○

SOCIAL
Charisma ●●●●○
Manipulation ●●●●●
Appearance ○○○○○

MENTAL
Perception ●●○○○
Intelligence ●●○○○
Wits ●●●●○

ABILITIES

TALENTS
Alertness ●●●○○
Athletics ○○○○○
Brawl ●○○○○
Dodge ●●●○○
Empathy ●●○○○
Expression ●●●○○
Intimidation ●○○○○
Leadership ●○○○○
Streetwise ●●○○○
Subterfuge ○○○○○

SKILLS
Animal Ken ○○○○○
Crafts ●○○○○
Drive ○○○○○
Etiquette ●●○○○
Firearms ○○○○○
Melee ○○○○○
Performance ●●●○○
Security ●○○○○
Stealth ○○○○○
Survival ○○○○○

KNOWLEDGES
Academics ●○○○○
Computer ●○○○○
Finance ○○○○○
Investigation ●●●○○
Law ○○○○○
Linguistics ●●○○○
Medicine ○○○○○
Occult ○○○○○
Politics ●○○○○
Science ○○○○○

ADVANTAGES

BACKGROUNDS
Fame ●○○○○
Generation ●○○○○
Mentor ●○○○○
Resources ●●●○○
○○○○○
○○○○○
○○○○○

DISCIPLINES
Obfuscate ●●○○○
Potence ●○○○○
Presence ●○○○○
○○○○○
○○○○○
○○○○○
○○○○○

VIRTUES
Conscience/Conviction ●●●○○

Self-Control/Instinct ●●●●○

Courage ●●○○○

MERITS/FLAWS

HUMANITY/PATH
●●●●●●●○○○

WILLPOWER
●●●●○○○○○○
□□□□□□□□□□

BLOOD POOL
□□□□□□□□□□
□□□□□□□□□□

HEALTH
Bruised □
Hurt -1 □
Injured -1 □
Wounded -2 □
Mauled -2 □
Crippled -5 □
Incapacitated □

EXPERIENCE

91

Mind's Eye Theatre — LAWS of the Night

Character Sheet 1

CONSCIENCE/CONVICTION ● ● ○ ○

SELF-CONTROL/INSTINCT ● ● ● ○ ○

COURAGE ● ● ● ● ○

BLOOD ● ● ● ● ● / ● ● ● ● ● / ● ● ○

WILLPOWER ● ● ○ ○ ○ ○ / □ □ □ □ □ / □ □ □ □ □ / □ □ □ □ □

NAME _____
CHARACTER **Skin**
CHRONICLE _____
CLAN **Nosferatu**
GENERATION **12th**
AGE _____
NATURE **Loner**
DEMEANOR **Trickster**

PATH/HUMANITY ● ● ● ○

PHYSICAL
Dextrous
Graceful
Resilient

SOCIAL
Charming x2   Persuasive
Eloquent   Witty x2
Expressive   Repugnant x3 [N]

MENTAL
Alert   Observant
Cever
Creative x2

ABILITIES
Expression   Stealth x2
Investigation Subterfuge x2
Linguistics x3
Performance (Acting)

BACKGROUNDS
Fame x1
Generation x1
Mentor x1
Resources x3

INFLUENCES
_____
_____
_____

DISCIPLINES
Obfuscate (Cloak of Shadows.
Unseen Presence)
Potence (Prowess)
Presence (Awe)

MERITS & FLAWS
_____

Mind's Eye Theatre — LAWS of the Night

Character Sheet 2

CONSCIENCE/CONVICTION ● ● ○ ○ ○

SELF-CONTROL/INSTINCT ● ● ○ ○ ○

COURAGE ● ● ● ● ○

BLOOD ● ● ● ● ● / ● ● ● ● ● / ● ● ● ● ● / ● ● ● ● ●

WILLPOWER ● ● ● ● ● / ● ○ ○ ○ ○ / □ □ □ □ □ / □ □ □ □ □

NAME _____
CHARACTER **Brood Hen**
CHRONICLE _____
CLAN **Nosferatu**
GENERATION **9th**
AGE _____
NATURE **Autocrat**
DEMEANOR **Fanatic**

PATH/HUMANITY ● ● ● ○

PHYSICAL
Enduring
Nimble
Steady

SOCIAL
Beguiling   Repugnant x3 [N]
Commanding x2
Dignified x2

MENTAL
Attentive   Patient
Cuning x3   Wily
Knowledgeable

ABILITIES
Animal Ken   Stealth
Etiquette   Subterfuge
Expression
Politics

BACKGROUNDS
Contacts x3
Fame x1
Generation x4

INFLUENCES
_____
_____
_____

DISCIPLINES
Animalism (Feral Whispers.
The Beckoning)
Obfuscate (Cloak of Shadows)

MERITS & FLAWS
_____

Brood Hen

Quote: *Our clan must ally to ensure our survival; the needs of the brood must come first!*

Prelude: Before your Embrace, you were insecure enough to define your identity by the various groups to which you belonged. You had a vicious habit of playing politics and are ruthlessly efficient at gathering dirt on anyone who would destroy your authority. After your Embrace, you naturally gravitated toward a brood of Nosferatu desperately in need of organization. Now you play clan politics with an edge... and you don't care who gets cut to pieces in your ascension to power.

You're well-connected with other Nosferatu and won't let anyone forget it. While you can call upon the resources of your local brood, you also insist that any other Nosferatu in the city should be an integral part of its activities. You speak about your "clan" as though every Sewer Rat carries a membership card and attends regular meetings. While all Nosferatu in a brood are supposed to be equals, you're loyal enough to consider yourself more equal than others.

Concept: You run contrary to many of the standard ideas of Nosferatu society. For you, the brood must always come first. Your coterie will ask you to help them with many of their problems, but for every dilemma you solve for them, you must insist that they do something to help "the Nosferatu." The upside of this is that you're intimately familiar with all the resources the Nosferatu of your city have, from the slums to the sewers.

Roleplaying Hints: While dealing with your coterie, you're fairly easygoing, but you take a little too much pride in describing how much "Clan Nosferatu" has accomplished. And unfortunately, you're far too good at trading information for them to shut you out of the local Hostings. While your attitude toward politics is atypical for your clan, you're far too much of an individual to let the others sway you.

Equipment: maps of a few insignificant sewer tunnels (to parcel out to the neonates), little black book, cell phone, horned-rim glasses

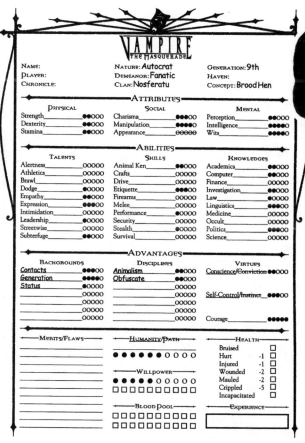

VAMPIRE THE MASQUERADE

NAME:
PLAYER:
CHRONICLE:

NATURE: Autocrat
DEMEANOR: Fanatic
CLAN: Nosferatu

GENERATION: 9th
HAVEN:
CONCEPT: Brood Hen

ATTRIBUTES

PHYSICAL
Strength ●●○○○
Dexterity ●●○○○
Stamina ●●○○○

SOCIAL
Charisma ●●●○○
Manipulation ●●●●○
Appearance ○○○○○

MENTAL
Perception ●●○○○
Intelligence ●●●●○
Wits ●●●●○

ABILITIES

TALENTS
Alertness ○○○○○
Athletics ○○○○○
Brawl ○○○○○
Dodge ●○○○○
Empathy ●●○○○
Expression ●●●○○
Intimidation ○○○○○
Leadership ●○○○○
Streetwise ○○○○○
Subterfuge ●●○○○

SKILLS
Animal Ken ●●○○○
Crafts ○○○○○
Drive ○○○○○
Etiquette ●●●○○
Firearms ○○○○○
Melee ○○○○○
Performance ●○○○○
Security ○○○○○
Stealth ●○○○○
Survival ○○○○○

KNOWLEDGES
Academics ●●○○○
Computer ●●○○○
Finance ○○○○○
Investigation ●●○○○
Law ●○○○○
Linguistics ●●●○○
Medicine ○○○○○
Occult ○○○○○
Politics ●●●○○
Science ○○○○○

ADVANTAGES

BACKGROUNDS
Contacts ●●●○○
Generation ●●●●○
Status ●○○○○
_____ ○○○○○
_____ ○○○○○
_____ ○○○○○
_____ ○○○○○

DISCIPLINES
Animalism ●●○○○
Obfuscate ●●○○○
_____ ○○○○○
_____ ○○○○○
_____ ○○○○○
_____ ○○○○○

VIRTUES
Conscience/Conviction ●●○○○

Self-Control/Instinct ●●●○○

Courage ●●●●●

MERITS/FLAWS

HUMANITY/PATH
●●●●●●○○○○

WILLPOWER
●●●●●○○○○○
□□□□□□□□□□

BLOOD POOL
□□□□□□□□□□
□□□□□□□□□□

HEALTH
Bruised □
Hurt -1 □
Injured -1 □
Wounded -2 □
Mauled -2 □
Crippled -5 □
Incapacitated □

EXPERIENCE

Leif Jones 2000

DARK CRUSADER

Quote: *I am the reflection of your sins, come to take you to Hell.*

Prelude: Even before your Embrace, you viewed the world through the eyes of a pariah. Held in contempt by parents and peers alike, you were the target of ridicule and ostracism. The world and you simply found little of mutual liking, and you preferred the solace of escapism, retreating into a dreamland of obscure authors, comic books and fantasy.

One night, you found yourself in a situation all too real, as the wrong people took an exception to your presence. You had been beaten up before, but the gang beating you received was truly savage. Beaten beyond human endurance, you crawled miserably on broken hands and shattered knees, seeking help or perhaps just a place to die. You found both. Taken into the world of the Damned, you were re-formed from the worm you had been into a twisted but powerful night-moth. Now, armed with righteous fury, you crusade against bigots, brutes, rapists and others you deem as "unfit to live."

Concept: Don't let anyone convince you that the World of Darkness is painted in shades of gray, that the bad guys are just misunderstood, that moral-

ity is relative or that everyone has a rationale for what they do. They're just trying to confuse you. You've got a talent for two things: finding "evil" and destroying it. Once you've done the first, you won't hesitate to do the second. While you're eager to apply a few Size 12 boots and judicious Potence to the most horrific problems you face, you're also a keen (and overconfident) investigator.

Roleplaying Hints: You see the world in black and white. You may be damned for all eternity, but that's not going to stop you from doing what you think is right... even if everyone else thinks it's wrong. Obviously, you see yourself as a hero, but you're more of a villain to everyone else. With your propensity for violence and your vigilante methods, you'll stop at nothing to destroy what you don't understand. You're inexorably drawn to the most horrific and despicable evils on the planet... and won't admit that you're one of them.

Equipment: leather jacket, black jeans, heavy boots, black gloves, black mask (for added mystique), length of chain, lead pipe

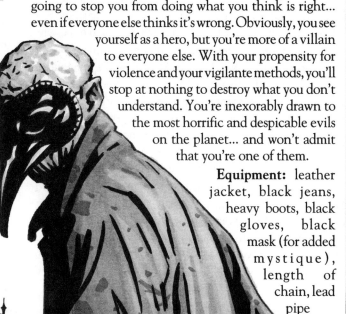

VAMPIRE
THE MASQUERADE

NAME:
PLAYER:
CHRONICLE:

NATURE: Bravo
DEMEANOR: Judge
CLAN: Nosferatu

GENERATION: 10th
HAVEN:
CONCEPT: Crusader

ATTRIBUTES

PHYSICAL
- Strength ●●●●○
- Dexterity ●●●○○
- Stamina ●●●○○

SOCIAL
- Charisma ●●●○○
- Manipulation ●●●○○
- Appearance ○○○○○

MENTAL
- Perception ●●○○○
- Intelligence ●●○○○
- Wits ●●●●○

ABILITIES

TALENTS
- Alertness ●●○○○
- Athletics ●●○○○
- Brawl ●●●○○
- Dodge ●●●○○
- Empathy ○○○○○
- Expression ○○○○○
- Intimidation ●●●○○
- Leadership ●○○○○
- Streetwise ●●○○○
- Subterfuge ○○○○○

SKILLS
- Animal Ken ○○○○○
- Crafts ○○○○○
- Drive ●○○○○
- Etiquette ○○○○○
- Firearms ●●○○○
- Melee ●●●○○
- Performance ○○○○○
- Security ○○○○○
- Stealth ●○○○○
- Survival ○○○○○

KNOWLEDGES
- Academics ●●○○○
- Computer ○○○○○
- Finance ○○○○○
- Investigation ●●●●○
- Law ○○○○○
- Linguistics ○○○○○
- Medicine ●○○○○
- Occult ●●○○○
- Politics ○○○○○
- Science ●●○○○

ADVANTAGES

BACKGROUNDS
- *Generation* ●●●○○
- *Mentor* ●○○○○
- *Resources* ●●●○○
- *Retainers* ●○○○○

DISCIPLINES
- Potence ●●●○○
- ___ ○○○○○
- ___ ○○○○○
- ___ ○○○○○
- ___ ○○○○○
- ___ ○○○○○

VIRTUES
- Conscience/Conviction ●●●●○
- Self-Control/Instinct ●●○○○
- Courage ●●●●○

MERITS/FLAWS

HUMANITY/PATH
●●●●●●●○○○

WILLPOWER
●●●●●○○○○○
□□□□□□□□□□

BLOOD POOL
□□□□□□□□□□
□□□□□□□□□□

HEALTH
Bruised		□
Hurt	-1	□
Injured	-1	□
Wounded	-2	□
Mauled	-2	□
Crippled	-5	□
Incapacitated		□

EXPERIENCE

LEIF JONES 2000

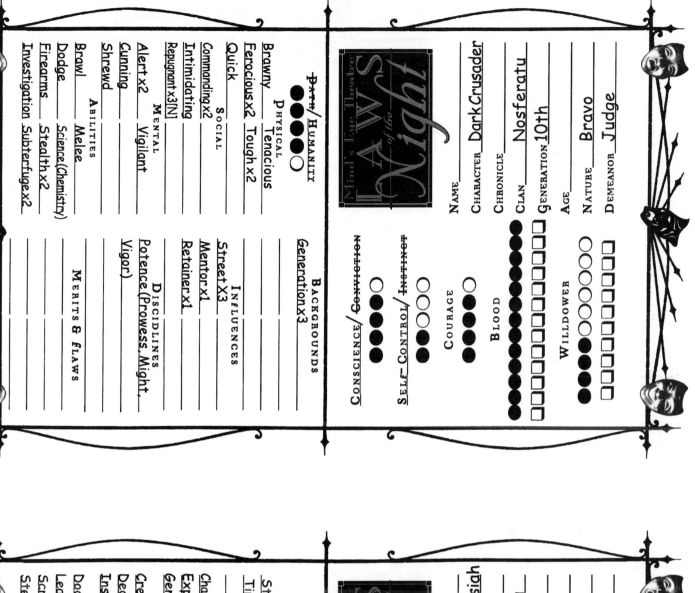

LAWS of the Night — Mind's Eye Theatre

Name ___
Character DarkCrusader
Chronicle ___
Clan Nosferatu
Generation 10th
Age ___
Nature Bravo
Demeanor Judge

Conscience/~~Conviction~~
Self-Control/Instinct
Courage
Blood
Willpower

Path/Humanity ●●●●○

Physical
Ferocious x2 Tough x2
Brawny Tenacious
Quick

Social
Commanding x2
Intimidating
Repugnant x3[N]

Mental
Alert x2 Vigilant

Abilities
Shrewd
Cunning
Brawl   Melee
Dodge   Science(Chemistry)
Firearms   Stealth x2
Investigation Subterfuge x2

Backgrounds
Generation x3

Influences
Street X3
Mentor x1
Retainer x1

Disciplines
Potence(Prowess, Might, Vigor)

Merits & Flaws

LAWS of the Night — Mind's Eye Theatre

Name ___
Character Leper Messiah
Chronicle ___
Clan Nosferatu
Generation 13th
Age ___
Nature Conniver
Demeanor Rebel

Conscience/~~Conviction~~
Self-Control/Instinct
Courage
Blood
Willpower

Path/Humanity ●●●●○

Physical
Steady x2
Tireless

Social
Charismatic x2 Persuasive
Expressive Repugnant x3[N]
Genial

Mental
Creative Observant
Dedicated Patient x2
Insightful Wise

Abilities
Dodge Streetwise
Leadership Survival
Scrounge
Stealth

Backgrounds
Herd x2
Retainers x4

Influences

Disciplines
Animalism(Feral Whispers,
The Beckoning)
Potence(Prowess)

Merits & Flaws

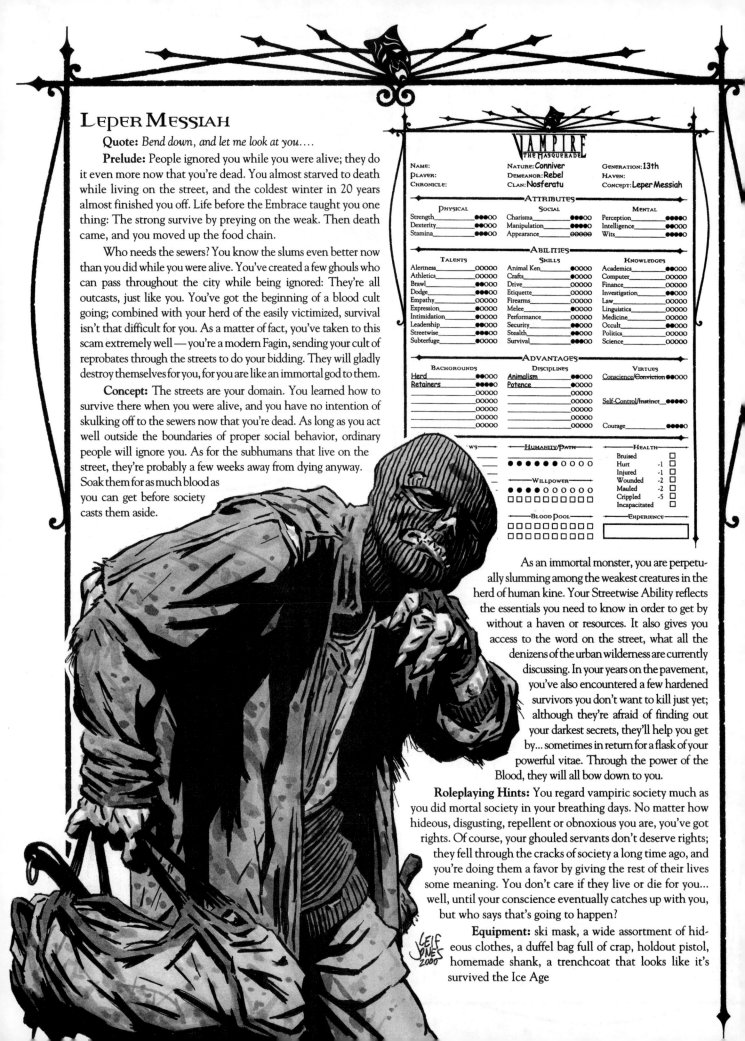

LEPER MESSIAH

Quote: *Bend down, and let me look at you....*

Prelude: People ignored you while you were alive; they do it even more now that you're dead. You almost starved to death while living on the street, and the coldest winter in 20 years almost finished you off. Life before the Embrace taught you one thing: The strong survive by preying on the weak. Then death came, and you moved up the food chain.

Who needs the sewers? You know the slums even better now than you did while you were alive. You've created a few ghouls who can pass throughout the city while being ignored: They're all outcasts, just like you. You've got the beginning of a blood cult going; combined with your herd of the easily victimized, survival isn't that difficult for you. As a matter of fact, you've taken to this scam extremely well — you're a modern Fagin, sending your cult of reprobates through the streets to do your bidding. They will gladly destroy themselves for you, for you are like an immortal god to them.

Concept: The streets are your domain. You learned how to survive there when you were alive, and you have no intention of skulking off to the sewers now that you're dead. As long as you act well outside the boundaries of proper social behavior, ordinary people will ignore you. As for the subhumans that live on the street, they're probably a few weeks away from dying anyway. Soak them for as much blood as you can get before society casts them aside.

VAMPIRE
THE MASQUERADE

NAME:	NATURE: Conniver	GENERATION: 13th
PLAYER:	DEMEANOR: Rebel	HAVEN:
CHRONICLE:	CLAN: Nosferatu	CONCEPT: Leper Messiah

ATTRIBUTES

PHYSICAL		SOCIAL		MENTAL	
Strength	●●●○○	Charisma	●●●○○	Perception	●●●●○
Dexterity	●●○○○	Manipulation	●●●●○	Intelligence	●●●○○
Stamina	●●●○○	Appearance	○○○○○	Wits	●●●●○

ABILITIES

TALENTS		SKILLS		KNOWLEDGES	
Alertness	○○○○○	Animal Ken	●○○○○	Academics	●●○○○
Athletics	○○○○○	Crafts	●○○○○	Computer	○○○○○
Brawl	●●○○○	Drive	○○○○○	Finance	○○○○○
Dodge	●●●○○	Etiquette	○○○○○	Investigation	●●○○○
Empathy	○○○○○	Firearms	○○○○○	Law	○○○○○
Expression	●○○○○	Melee	●○○○○	Linguistics	○○○○○
Intimidation	●○○○○	Performance	○○○○○	Medicine	○○○○○
Leadership	●●○○○	Security	●●○○○	Occult	●●○○○
Streetwise	●●●○○	Stealth	●●●○○	Politics	○○○○○
Subterfuge	●●○○○	Survival	●●●○○	Science	○○○○○

ADVANTAGES

BACKGROUNDS		DISCIPLINES		VIRTUES	
Herd	●●○○○	Animalism	●●○○○	Conscience/~~Conviction~~	●●○○○
Retainers	●●●●○	Potence	●○○○○		
	○○○○○		○○○○○		
	○○○○○		○○○○○	Self-Control/~~Instinct~~	●●●●●
	○○○○○		○○○○○		
	○○○○○		○○○○○		
	○○○○○		○○○○○	Courage	●●●●○

...WS	HUMANITY/PATH	HEALTH

HUMANITY/PATH
●●●●●●○○○○

WILLPOWER
●●●○○○○○○○
□□□□□□□□□□

BLOOD POOL
□□□□□□□□□□
□□□□□□□□□□

HEALTH		
Bruised		□
Hurt	-1	□
Injured	-1	□
Wounded	-2	□
Mauled	-2	□
Crippled	-5	□
Incapacitated		□

EXPERIENCE

As an immortal monster, you are perpetually slumming among the weakest creatures in the herd of human kine. Your Streetwise Ability reflects the essentials you need to know in order to get by without a haven or resources. It also gives you access to the word on the street, what all the denizens of the urban wilderness are currently discussing. In your years on the pavement, you've also encountered a few hardened survivors you don't want to kill just yet; although they're afraid of finding out your darkest secrets, they'll help you get by... sometimes in return for a flask of your powerful vitae. Through the power of the Blood, they will all bow down to you.

Roleplaying Hints: You regard vampiric society much as you did mortal society in your breathing days. No matter how hideous, disgusting, repellent or obnoxious you are, you've got rights. Of course, your ghouled servants don't deserve rights; they fell through the cracks of society a long time ago, and you're doing them a favor by giving the rest of their lives some meaning. You don't care if they live or die for you... well, until your conscience eventually catches up with you, but who says that's going to happen?

Equipment: ski mask, a wide assortment of hideous clothes, a duffel bag full of crap, holdout pistol, homemade shank, a trenchcoat that looks like it's survived the Ice Age

LEIF
JONES
2000

Venerable Nosferatu

Existence as a Nosferatu is difficult, but fortunately, centuries of Nosferatu history serve as an example to the latest generation of neonates. Stories and legends are whispered in the depths of the sewers late at night, and the greatest ones involve the most powerful, legendary and infamous Creeps and Sewer Rats of vampiric society. Although a few of these monsters have met Final Death, they've done so with a style and grace that is uniquely Nosferatu... or, at least, in a vile and disgusting manner that only another Nosferatu could truly appreciate.

Baba Yaga

The Hag is dead, but her legacy lives on. In 1998, a legendary vampire sired by Nosferatu himself met Final Death, slain under the talons of Lupines. For centuries, she had directed her vampiric minions throughout Russia. The amount of supernatural activity in that nation was so great that a spiritual Shadow Curtain surrounded the Soviet Union, isolating ancient sacred sites from the rest of the world.

The Hag's command of Thaumaturgy was so impressive that she was often mistaken for a sorceress. Her mastery of Obfuscate allowed her to enact grand schemes without attracting the attention of the mortal populace. As a fourth-generation vampire, she was allegedly one of three Nosferatu who escaped their sire's blood bond, acting with a vengeance even the legendary Nictuku could not equal.

Now Baba Yaga is gone, the Shadow Curtain has fallen, and the Soviet Union has fragmented into chaos. Russian Nosferatu no longer need fear her; instead, they face the monumental task of trying to establish new domains, creating a series of independent broods across Asia. To the west lies the Camarilla, a society from which they have been isolated for centuries. To the east lie the dangerous lands of the Cathayans, who are eager to seize the domains Baba Yaga no longer protects. With the turmoil that surrounds them, most Russian Nosferatu have wisely decided to remain hidden and autarkis. They have watched one overlord die; they are not so eager to welcome another. A few have begun traveling to broods in other parts of the world. As these Nosferatu emissaries learn of events outside Russia, they tell old legends of Baba Yaga again and again.

Emmett, Autarkis Traitor

Emmett is an outsider, even among the Nosferatu. He owes allegiance to no coterie, brood, domain ruler or vampiric sect — ultimately, his only allegiance is to himself. This doesn't prevent him from dealing in vampiric politics, since Emmett is a master at the art of brokering information. Camarilla, Sabbat, anarch or autarkis — he'll swap legends and lore with any Nosferatu in desperate need of information. A loner and a wanderer, Emmett is polite enough to find havens in the domains of various Nosferatu kingdoms but also has a dangerous habit of neglecting to tell princes and archbishops about his subterranean sojourns.

Skulking through any city where the scandals are thick, he'll eagerly trade data with Kindred and Cainites who are not Nosferatu, although he sets his prices very steep. Emmett can find out just about anything, but he always asks for a favor in return, usually involving an investigation of dark secrets that could never be traced

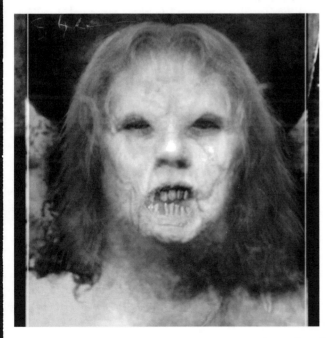

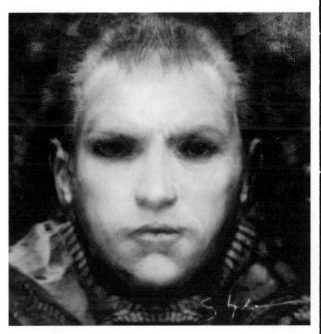

back to him. On a few occasions, coteries and packs have tried to offer him false information... and in return, have found themselves the target of calumny and scandal in every city where a Nosferatu is present.

As a neonate, Emmett has also been very active in a Nosferatu computer node called SchreckNET, an elaborate data hierarchy where Sewer Rats and Creeps alike trade rumors and innuendo. Spending much of his night online, he can access vast amounts of lore from across Europe and North America, lurking in countless chat rooms and virtual domains simultaneously. Like any good Nosferatu hacker, he's also learned to construct false identities in online conversations... and is terribly good at spotting the ones used by other cybercreeps.

Recent events have put Emmett in the nacreous limelight, mainly because he claims to be the only survivor of an infamous Hosting held in the depths of Manhattan's underground. A Hosting of Nosferatu storytellers and historians turned to tragedy when a series of tunnels collapsed in the kingdom's sanctum sanctorum. While no one has found the bodies — or the perpetrators — Emmett claims that the gathering was betrayed to the legendary Nictuku. Allegedly, a vengeful group of autarkis Nosferatu was responsible, but such treachery was unthinkable among the vampires of the clan... until now.

Emmett's outspoken position has gained him enmity both in the Camarilla and the Sabbat, especially among independent and anarch Nosferatu. Thus, he has been forced to hide from many of the influential vampires of his own clan, becoming an infamous autarkis himself. Desperate to gain enough reputation and information to get others to believe him, Emmett has once again taken to trading information outside the clan and is eager for any news of suspicious activities below ground. Woe be to the unfortunate coterie who decides to explore a subterranean labyrinth in exchange for the secrets he possesses....

CALIBAN, SABBAT CRUSADER

While Creeps and Sewer Rats may occasionally conspire below ground, they are still at war in the surface world. Truces conducted between individuals fall apart when Sabbat crusaders muster in the barrens outside of a Camarilla domain. While diplomatic Sabbat Nosferatu may convince a brood of Camarilla Rats to exchange dark secrets, other Creeps are infamous wherever they travel and are trusted by no one outside of their own sect. So it is with Caliban, crusader *extraordinaire* for the Sword of Caine.

The tunnels beneath the domains of powerful princes are often well-defended against outsiders, but other Nosferatu are skilled at seeing through layers of traps, insidious obfuscation and ingenious strategies of defense. Caliban is a Sabbat ductus who specializes in subterranean raids, no matter how dangerous. In her rise to infamy and power, she has led at least a dozen War Parties through the netherworlds of Camarilla cities. Her body count not only includes a few choice examples of Kindred nobility but a few other, unknown monsters lurking in the sewers, from clutches of ghouled albino alligators to ruthless shapechanging rats, from vast spore-infested fungal chambers to hideous cults of subterranean ghouls. Caliban fights at the vanguard of her pack, accepts no quarter and demands fanatical bloodlust from all who follow her into battle.

KHALID

While the Assamites may have established the most influential clan in shadowed Araby, they are by no means the only one. Khalid of Clan Nosferatu is one of the most notable Arabian Cainites. Although he has long since joined the politics of the West — and still serves as the Nosferatu primogen of Chicago — his legacy is inseparably intertwined with the history of the Middle East.

Before his Embrace in 1191, Khalid was a bloody butcher who easily lived up to the hideous reputation Christian knights attributed to Muslim warriors. Few could match his appetite for atrocity, for Khalid freely performed cruel deeds in service to his god. The Crusades brought many Camarilla Kindred to the Holy Land for the first time. Among them was Alexius, a

Byzantine Nosferatu and former prelate of the Eastern Orthodox Church. Alexius believed that the only way to weaken the paynim nations was to corrupt and suborn its leaders through the Embrace. Alexius, fascinated by Khalid's extreme cruelty, rewarded it by baptizing him into darkness.

Khalid, horrified at the curse bestowed upon him, exacted his rage on his own soldiers before fleeing into the desert. There he starved himself of blood as penitence for his cruel life. The intervention of a reclusive Jewish hermit saved the neonate, and Khalid, starving for an explanation of the mysteries he had encountered, began to study the occult under the old man's tutelage. At first, Khalid immersed himself in gematria, the Kabbala and other forms of mysticism. His search for meaning eventually led him to the myth of Golconda. This vision then became an unlifelong quest for him.

For six centuries, Khalid wandered the world; along the way, he witnessed the best and worst examples of the Camarilla's meddling in human history. By the end of the 19th century, his search led him to the city of Chicago, where he had heard of an Inconnu slumbering beneath the city. Allegedly, this creature bestowed hints of Golconda to his petitioners. Khalid sought wisdom; instead, he found a city still reeling from the Great Fire of 1871.

Khalid's carefully nurtured morality compelled him to help rebuild the city. After helping a local brood restore their underground kingdom, he was drawn into the politics of the local Kindred, from the reign of Prince Maxwell to the fall of the infamous Prince Lodin. While Khalid has become a master of vampiric politics, he is now ready to leave Chicago again, and he is hungry for any knowledge of Golconda that he can find. For true Nosferatu martyrs, politics are but a diversion to fill the empty nights of eternity. Khalid watches and waits for another chance to pursue the deepest of vampiric mysteries.

MALACHITE

Throughout the Dark Ages, Constantinople played a pivotal role in the history of European Kindred. While many vampiric historians are eager to regale listeners with the legend of Michael, the Byzantine Methuselah of Clan Toreador, they typically forget the hidden history of his city. Medieval Constantinople had one of the most extensive systems of viaducts and storm tunnels in all of Europe, and hidden within them, Malachite of Clan Nosferatu has watched the secret history of the Eastern European Kindred.

Malachite was the chosen name of Maleki, a former prelate of Byzantium. As a talented scholar of the occult, he had entered a blood oath with Magnus, a powerful Lasombra who hid in the shadows of the Eastern Orthodox Church. Magnus offered him a position of great power, but it depended upon Maleki's forced acceptance of religious doctrine he could not support. Maleki was a staunch supporter of Iconoclasm: Simply put, he believed that religious worship required the veneration of icons. After seeing many monks forced from the city for espousing this belief, he publicly decried such oppression as an obvious attempt to usurp their political influence. Maleki's bold stance earned Magnus' scorn, and the Lasombra

punished the prelate. Instead of killing Maleki outright, the Lasombra forced his apprentice's Embrace at the hands of a diseased Nosferatu.

As Maleki contemplated his cruel fate and hideous visage, he underwent a profound psychological transformation. His punishment did not reduce his commitment, but instead made him a martyr for his cause. Renaming himself Malachite, he acted as the "Rock of Constantinople," continuing to war with Magnus for control of the Orthodox Church. Magnus made a grave error, not realizing that while a Nosferatu's Embrace may break a lesser man, many so-called "Sewer Rats" have found new reserves of spiritual strength in the depths of their despair.

The years that followed brought turmoil to the Orthodox Church, but these religious disputes were soon eclipsed by political upheaval. Malachite has seen firsthand the fall of Constantinople to the Turks and its transformation to a city where Islam has overshadowed the Eastern Orthodox faith. Yet stubbornly, he has remained in what is now Istanbul. His epic adherence to his religious principles has made him an anachronism, but he serves the Divine today just as reverently as he did centuries ago.

In the modern age, the extensive waterways beneath Istanbul are still dominated by the Nosferatu. Above ground, Istanbul's Kindred are predominately Muslim, but the Nosferatu who have remained hidden have kept their religious beliefs secret from the surface vampires for centuries. The broods beneath Istanbul reflect a wide array of faiths, and the underworld's population reflects the religious evolution of the city. Despite differences of faith, the Nosferatu are united by a common cause: the maintenance of their underground kingdom. While the world above continues to change, Malachite remains steadfast in his faith and continues to pray as he did centuries ago. The Rock of Constantinople has not been moved.

ZELIOS

The Nosferatu are known for more than just their ability to trade secrets. Because they must hide themselves from the world of men, they must also construct hidden places where they can survive. Throughout their history, they have influenced the architecture of human cities around the world, subtly altering the plans of major buildings to accommodate their own kind. The best known historical example of this is the work of Zelios, a Master Mason known for his architectural skills throughout both the Old World and the New World.

Zelios never took credit for the buildings he altered. He did, however, possess the ability to look at any architectural creation and devise subtle ways to improve it. After his Embrace, with all of eternity before him, he dedicated himself to the study of architecture and the perfection of his craft. In the 12th century, the Kindred of Europe made their homes in vast castles, sometimes the very castles where mortal nobility lived. By dominating mortals and ghouling their workers, vampires sometimes created hidden rooms where humans dared not tread. With an intuitive knowledge of both architecture and the occult science of geomancy, Zelios became famous throughout Europe for improving many of the continent's most notable castles.

Intrigue eventually forced Zelios from the Old World to the New World, where he was again commissioned to design elaborate structures for the Kindred. After a brief (and disastrous) attempt at politics as a Nosferatu primogen, he began a thriving career expanding and elaborating on the sewer systems of major cities. With the same care he lavished upon castles above ground, he manipulated his mortal pawns to make alterations to labyrinths below ground. His most elaborate effort includes many of the subway tunnels and sewer systems of New York, although sadly, much of his creation has since fallen into the hands of the Sabbat. Nonetheless, despite the distractions of intrigue, politics, occult deception and personal treachery, he has spent centuries mastering the art of architecture. His legacy lies in brick and mortar beneath the greatest cities of North America.

NOSFERATU

NAME: NATURE: GENERATION:

PLAYER: DEMEANOR: SIRE:

CHRONICLE: CONCEPT: HAVEN:

ATTRIBUTES

PHYSICAL
Strength _____ ●OOOO
Dexterity _____ ●OOOO
Stamina _____ ●OOOO

SOCIAL
Charisma _____ ●OOOO
Manipulation _____ ●OOOO
Appearance _____ OOOOO

MENTAL
Perception _____ ●OOOO
Intelligence _____ ●OOOO
Wits _____ ●OOOO

ABILITIES

TALENTS
Alertness _____ OOOOO
Athletics _____ OOOOO
Brawl _____ OOOOO
Dodge _____ OOOOO
Empathy _____ OOOOO
Expression _____ OOOOO
Intimidation _____ OOOOO
Leadership _____ OOOOO
Streetwise _____ OOOOO
Subterfuge _____ OOOOO

SKILLS
Animal Ken _____ OOOOO
Crafts _____ OOOOO
Drive _____ OOOOO
Etiquette _____ OOOOO
Firearms _____ OOOOO
Melee _____ OOOOO
Performance _____ OOOOO
Security _____ OOOOO
Stealth _____ OOOOO
Survival _____ OOOOO

KNOWLEDGES
Academics _____ OOOOO
Computer _____ OOOOO
Finance _____ OOOOO
Investigation _____ OOOOO
Law _____ OOOOO
Linguistics _____ OOOOO
Medicine _____ OOOOO
Occult _____ OOOOO
Politics _____ OOOOO
Science _____ OOOOO

ADVANTAGES

BACKGROUNDS
_____ OOOOO
_____ OOOOO
_____ OOOOO
_____ OOOOO
_____ OOOOO
_____ OOOOO
_____ OOOOO

DISCIPLINES
_____ OOOOO
_____ OOOOO
_____ OOOOO
_____ OOOOO
_____ OOOOO
_____ OOOOO
_____ OOOOO

VIRTUES
Conscience/Conviction ●OOOO

Self-Control/Instinct __ ●OOOO

Courage _____ ●OOOO

MERITS/FLAWS
_____
_____
_____
_____
_____
_____
_____
_____
_____

HUMANITY/PATH
_____
O O O O O O O O O O

WILLPOWER
O O O O O O O O O O
☐ ☐ ☐ ☐ ☐ ☐ ☐ ☐ ☐ ☐

BLOOD POOL
☐ ☐ ☐ ☐ ☐ ☐ ☐ ☐ ☐ ☐
☐ ☐ ☐ ☐ ☐ ☐ ☐ ☐ ☐ ☐

HEALTH
Bruised		☐
Hurt	-1	☐
Injured	-1	☐
Wounded	-2	☐
Mauled	-2	☐
Crippled	-5	☐
Incapacitated		☐

WEAKNESS
Appearance: 0.
Cannot improve Appearance with
experience points.

NOSFERATU

OTHER TRAITS

_____ OOOOO	_____ OOOOO	_____ OOOOO
_____ OOOOO	_____ OOOOO	_____ OOOOO
_____ OOOOO	_____ OOOOO	_____ OOOOO
_____ OOOOO	_____ OOOOO	_____ OOOOO
_____ OOOOO	_____ OOOOO	_____ OOOOO
_____ OOOOO	_____ OOOOO	_____ OOOOO
_____ OOOOO	_____ OOOOO	_____ OOOOO

RITUALS

NAME	LEVEL
_____	_____
_____	_____
_____	_____
_____	_____
_____	_____
_____	_____
_____	_____
_____	_____
_____	_____
_____	_____
_____	_____
_____	_____
_____	_____
_____	_____
_____	_____
_____	_____
_____	_____
_____	_____

EXPERIENCE

TOTAL: _____

TOTAL SPENT: _____

spent on:

_____

_____

_____

_____

_____

DERANGEMENTS

_____

_____

_____

_____

_____

_____

_____

BLOOD BONDS/ VINCULI

BOUND TO	RATING	BOUND TO	RATING
_____	_____	_____	_____
_____	_____	_____	_____
_____	_____	_____	_____
_____	_____	_____	_____

COMBAT

WEAPON	DAMAGE	RANGE	RATE	CLIP	CONCEAL

ARMOR

_____

_____

_____

_____

NOSFERATU

Expanded Background

ALLIES

_____
_____
_____
_____

CONTACTS

_____
_____
_____
_____

FAME

_____
_____
_____

HERD

_____
_____
_____

INFLUENCE

_____
_____
_____
_____

MENTOR

_____
_____
_____
_____

RESOURCES

_____
_____
_____

RETAINERS

_____
_____
_____

STATUS

_____
_____
_____

OTHER

_____
_____
_____
_____

Possessions

GEAR (CARRIED)

_____
_____
_____
_____
_____

FEEDING GROUNDS

_____
_____
_____

EQUIPMENT (OWNED)

_____
_____
_____
_____
_____

VEHICLES

_____
_____
_____

Havens

LOCATION

_____
_____
_____

DESCRIPTION

_____
_____
_____

NOSFERATU

HISTORY
PRELUDE

_____
_____
_____
_____
_____
_____
_____
_____
_____
_____
_____
_____
_____
_____
_____
_____

APPEARANCE

AGE_____   _____
APPARENT AGE_____   _____
DATE OF BIRTH_____   _____
RIP_____   _____
HAIR_____   _____
EYES_____   _____
RACE_____   _____
NATIONALITY_____   _____
HEIGHT_____   _____
WEIGHT_____   _____
SEX_____   _____

VISUALS

COTERIE CHART   CHARACTER SKETCH